HUSH-HUSH

The Story of LNER 10000

William Brown

Kestrel Railway Books
PO Box 269
SOUTHAMPTON
SO30 4XR

www.kestrelrailwaybooks.co.uk

Printed by the Amadeus Press

ISBN 978-1-905505-15-9

Front cover: *10000 at Kings Cross. From an original painting by M.A. Turner, Tel 01424 421950.*

Back Cover: *10000 at Darlington. Soon after the first run, a handrail was fitted on the front, and this can be seen here. (Ken Hoole Collection)*

Contents

Introduction

My first encounter with W1 No 10000 was in the Fifties. The small museum in Darlington town centre had several large-scale model locomotives in its window, one of which was No 10000. Having a fascination for railways, which had started very early in my life (I had not graduated to train spotter yet, being content to entertain myself with the products of Tri-ang) I was convinced that this space ship before me was a flight of someone's imagination. It remained so, in my mind, for a number of years. I recall, in the early 'Sixties, on a visit to Darlington Works, being told, from the train, "that brick building over there houses the boiler from Hush-Hush". By that time, I was out and about train spotting and was in too big a hurry to see as much as I could and as quickly as possible, to stop and think about what this meant. We all know what happens in mid- to late-teens and it was not until 1969, when I purchased my, still treasured, copies of

The British Steam Railway Locomotive, Volumes 1 & 2 (Ahrons/Nock) that Volume 2 yielded "L.N.E.R. ENGINE 10,000 GENERAL ARRANGEMENT DRAWING". Finally I understood, sadly, a few years too late to go and have a good look; the boiler had been lost. But it was at this time that 10000 became real to me. I have since read every article I could find about this locomotive, and they have all left me cold. I have always felt that I was reading no more than another superficial technical description padded out with the usual references to "the Galloping Sausage" and the popular misconceptions. Unfortunately I had to accept what I read, as I had little else to go on.

During my degree studies in the 'Seventies the reason for my dissatisfaction was made all too clear; in the reading of historiography it became obvious to me that the nearest to primary source material I was seeing with respect to 10000 were the photographs and,

North Road. *The adolescent Bill Brown standing behind Dave Greenfield on J39 64727 at North Road scrap yard, only a stone's throw from 10000's water tube boiler, which was still in use as a steam generator at Stooperdale, just around the corner. The year is 1962. (Author's Collection)*

Introduction

maybe, the General Arrangement and other drawings.

In 2004 a chance phone call was to result in my one-year fixed-term appointment as Mechanical Engineer at the National Railway Museum. 4472 was proving to be a handful and the staff needed an extra pair of hands, both on the locomotive and the computer, for the first year of the Nation's second period of ownership of this locomotive, and its last full year "in ticket". During the resulting two evenings a week away from home, I had some time to devote to research at York, and it was not long before the librarian, Phil Atkins, cottoned on to the fact that I was intrigued by 10000, as he saw me patiently making a list of the "HP Compound Locomotive" drawings from the Darlington drawing register, the hand written original of course! He said, "Have you seen the file?" I said, "What file?" **Eureka!** I had access to more "HP Compound Locomotive" primary source material than anyone could possibly imagine.

I soon discovered why people had missed the full story. The file, essentially the North Road works documentation, had to be maintained as it was received, and rightly so. That made sense as far as the organisation of the file was concerned, but the sheer volume of documents, compartmentalised, and much of it out of chronological order, made it impossible to get to grips with the whole story. I was given permission to photocopy the contents to create a quite separate file, in chronological order, which would be essential in helping to tell the story. I copied the contents, several hundred documents, meticulously leaving the originals as I found them. Later my wife, Kathleen, and I duly put the copies in chronological order. The hardest job was to stop oneself from getting side-tracked, as the content passing before the eyes was wonderful, the ever patient Kathleen even commented from time to time on what she was seeing. However the original memos from Gresley to Bulleid, Thompson, and the like, had to wait. I took the time to sample the drawing list I had made and was not disappointed. It looks like most of the drawings are in the museum archive, original hand drawn, ink on film. I had the documents and access to the drawings, I still had to fill in the background, but the whole story was now within my grasp.

Acquisition of copies of Gresley's papers to the Institution of Mechanical Engineers moved the story on in areas both familiar and, unbelievably, after half a century of railway studies, entirely new to me! This project takes us back to early times, to consider steam and machines, progressing to the LNWR in the last quarter of the 19th century and the Lancashire and Yorkshire and Great Northern Railways in the first decades of the 20th century. We will move to the United States in 1924, to Scotland and Darlington in 1926, Derby, the European mainland, the United States and the Great Northern Railway, now part of the LNER, revisited, between 1926 and 1929, the locomotive being on paper. With the locomotive as hardware, we visit Darlington and Scotland in 1929, and Doncaster in 1937 moving to Darlington again in 1941. Another trip to Scotland and then Doncaster will be revisited in 1959, and finally 60009 today. We will explore the need for high-pressure steam, compounding and how it works, and consider the options taken by various engineers, particularly in the northern hemisphere, including, of course, H.N. Gresley. We will see how the engineer searches out solutions, with help from, often, unexpected places. The rebuild will be considered and how that came about. The story ends for the locomotive at Doncaster in 1959, the water tube boiler at Darlington in 1965, but for the tender it still continues.

The principal source of information for this book was the 10000 file and drawings, held at the National Railway Museum Archive. I was given permission to publish images from the following sources, for which I send my heart-felt gratitude

- The Ken Hoole Collection
- Cite du Train, Musée du Chemin de fer, Mulhouse, France
- Thierry Stora
- LNWR Society

Other images are in the author's collection or copyright expired. Thank you to those who helped me to collect these.

William Brown BA
January 2010

Bibliography

A History of Technology, Volume IV, the Industrial Revolution c 1750 to c 1850 (Various), Oxford

B&O Power. Steam, Diesel and Electric Power of the Baltimore and Ohio Railroad 1829 –1964 by L.W. Sagle

Back Track, April/May 1995, Was there a future for Steam? by Michael Rutherford

British Steam Locomotive Builders by James W Lowe

The British Steam Railway Locomotive, Volumes 1 & 2, by E.L. Ahrons / O.S. Nock

Bulleid and the Turf Burner by Ernie Shepherd, Kestrel Railway Books

Compound Locomotives by John Van Riemsdijk

La Locomotive a Vapeur by André Chapelon (Author), George Carpenter (Translator)

Master Builders of Steam by H.A.V. Bulleid

Sir Nigel Gresley, The Engineer and his Family by Geoffrey Hughes

The British Railway Steam Locomotive Catalogue by Bertram Baxter

The Callendar Steam Tables (work by Callendar, 1939 edition)

The Chronicles of Boulton's Siding by Alfred Rosling Bennett

The Gresley Observer Issue 141 Autumn 2006

The LSWR at Nine Elms by Barry Curl, Kestrel Railway Books

The Premier Line by O.S. Nock

The Sentinel Volume 2 1930-1980 by A.R. & J.L. Thomas

Yeadon's Register of LNER locomotives (W1) by W.B. Yeadon

Useful web sites:

www.chemicalogic.com. (Steam properties)

www.dself.dsl.pipex.com. (Unusual steam locomotives)

CHAPTER I

The Search for Efficiency

A Few Preliminaries and Reminders

The good engineer will, somehow, instinctively know what is needed to make things more efficient. Quite where it all comes from I am not sure, significant training and education plus a lot of who knows what. No criticism intended, but financiers often lack these attributes and need more convincing arguments than those, which, to them, seem to be possibly misguided intuition. Of course engineers understand each other but have to use hard economics, including statistics, to convince the financial world. It seems to me that F.W. Webb of the London and North Western Railway (LNWR) knew precisely this. For the statistics to start working, large sample populations are needed to prove a principle. Webb must have had some of the stuff that Stephenson was made of, as he was persuasive enough to be allowed to produce as many of an experimental class as the LNWR could afford, in order to produce convincing evidence of the virtue of one group of machines relative to another.

Gresley, in the case of 10000, produced only one, in spite of his work with Webb. This was clearly due to the financial constraints of the time, but bearing in mind the need for safe statistical data, produced by larger numbers, one could wonder why he bothered. It has to be said that he made a determined effort to keep changes from the A1 basic design to a minimum in the hope that the positive benefits could be clearly demonstrated, but in one machine? I can hear the assertion that the data is insufficient echoing along the east coast main line to this day!

From the outset of the development of 10000, problems beset Gresley. At home, his circumstances were nothing short of a nightmare, and problems that he would normally deal with himself were consequently left to others, who might, or might not have supported his ideas, or even been capable. 10000 became significantly different to the A1, with which it was intended to be a direct comparison. By the time construction was completed, the A1 had evolved into the A3, faster and more economic than the A1; both had developed along different paths and thus the gulf between them became wider. 10000 was severely compromised for almost two years of its early life with at least one massive and highly-significant schoolboy

error on the part of those delegated to ensure the careful and considered approach necessary for success. Bear in mind that first impressions take some shifting, whether they ultimately turn out to be right or wrong. The basis of the design of 10000 was to apply the latest thermodynamic thinking to a machine. For this reason we must look at the basics of thermodynamics in order to remind us of the potential that Gresley was to try to unleash. Of course we should give a thought to André Chapelon whilst examining this as he was exchanging ideas, one way or another, with Gresley over a significant period.

It was also necessary to use existing manufacturing facilities and be able to make comparisons to produce cost justification analysis for the new design. Thus we had a new boiler only, applied to a standard Pacific chassis with high-efficiency compound cylinders previously tried, tested and approved. Yes, compounds worked, and quite why Hughes misled his audience at the Institution of Mechanical Engineers, back in 1910, and thus effectively rang the death knell for steam, we may never know. However, Gresley was not put off and a decade or so later the compound was to get a chance with the LNER. The new boiler could have been in one of several similar arrangements or have been forced to some other maximum pressure and we will consider the options. As you will see, the continuous expansion of so-called compound cylinders was essential and as with the boilers we will look at the options. It is frightening to think of the tons of coal wasted in our failure to adopt more of these superb machines, regardless of economic philosophy. The examples built outside of the UK lasted for several decades, some for half a century and to the end of steam in their respective countries.

The W1 developed along a completely different evolutionary path to simple cylinder, fire-tube boiler machines, and to follow this we must take a journey to the past to establish the origin. To begin we must go a long way back in time from today's Eurostar to IC 225, IC 125, IC APT, English Electric Napier Deltic, Gresley, A4, P2, W1, and before this, A1, Raven Atlantic, Worsdell 4-4-0, Fletcher 2-4-0, Bouch 0-6-0, Stephenson 2-2-0, Hackworth 0-4-0, Stephenson 0-4-0, Trevithick 0-4-0, Watt Stationary Engine, and before even this…

In the Beginning, Almost, There was Steam

Although existing at very high pressures, under the earth, steam was contained at atmospheric pressure on the surface, and at this time the use of it for power was limited. Old Faithful Geyser has been around for quite some time now, and others like it for millennia. The billowing steam gives clues to engineers, and these are fundamental to Engineering Science. What has an old geyser got to do with things?

Whilst the steam bursts from the planet at great velocity, it is not long before it slows down and returns to Earth. Why does it not keep going forever upwards? Of course, we now know that it is gravity that does the trick. Make no mistake, gravity is not a man made invention, we currently have no way of controlling it, we simply take observations in order to predict behaviour. Luckily for us the behaviour of gravity is predictable and mathematical models can tell us how it will behave in given circumstances. It is gravity that gives things weight, even the air around us. Gravity exists wherever there is a mass, and planet Earth is massive. The mass of planet Earth is so big that for the vast majority of cases the gravitational attraction on the planet overwhelms all other earthly masses. Gravity is a force and it accelerates everything around it, towards the centre, at very approximately 10 metres per second per second, don't ask why, it just does. Now, if the steam of Old Faithful leaves the ground at 100 metres per second, then after one second it will slow down by 10 metres per second to 90 metres per second. Work this through and you will find that, after ten seconds, the steam will be stationary. Give it another second and it is on the way back to the ground at 10 metres per second, after ten seconds it returns to ground at 100 metres per second. Wind and heat interfere with the process, but remove their effect and what I describe is essentially what you get.

An important clue for engineering scientists comes from the observation that the steam returns to the ground. In fact, with the exception of flying objects with characteristics that prevent it, everything heads Earthwards. Thus it follows that the air around us must be returning to ground as well. Indeed it is, and all of those molecules each being pulled to Earth, over the whole of Earth's surface, result in air pressure. The scientific standard for pressure is, in fact, one atmosphere, that is the pressure exerted by the atmosphere in defined circumstances. For our purposes one atmosphere is very roughly 15 pounds per square inch at the Earth's surface.

Where geysers burst out of hot water pools, a significant amount of the pool is dragged into the air along with the steam. The steam seems to grab hold of the water as it shoots upwards. This is due to friction (once called "sticktion", which much better describes the effect, but possibly not the science). Science can model friction, but, unlike gravity, with a better understanding of what is going on. This gives us a clue as to how the steam injector works. It also picks up water, passing through the device on its way from the boiler to the boiler. The boiler to the boiler you may ask? You will have to see Bernoulli's Extended Theorem if you want a scientific explanation of this, sufficient to say boiler pressure becomes velocity in a nozzle and thus overcomes the pressure of the boiler into which it is returned, along with the water, picked up on its way.

The Origins of Railways and Engineering Science

Evidence suggests that the first primitive tramways date back several thousand years. What were once considered to be ruts, worn into stone by cartwheels, are now thought to have been deliberately hewn, to guide the vehicle along the road. In the case of the Romans, to control the traffic, slowing down the wild, young chariot riders who tended to race around in built up areas, at risk to themselves and everyone around them. The early forms of motive power were animals, including people if economics dictated this. Where the cost of animals became prohibitive, finance was provided to make machines driven by the power of nature. Wind, water, fire and gravity were at Man's disposal, though in the early days they were poorly understood and consequently less efficient in many cases than they could be. Science, which is simply the knowledge and understanding of nature through observation and the man-made rules that result, was studied from early times but only got teeth when commerce benefited. Eventually, Man produced the heat engine. For steam this was in the eighteenth century.

A History of Technology, Volume IV, the Industrial Revolution c1750 to c1850 yields the following, which I have edited to bring out the main points as I see them.

"In 1765, Gabriel Jars (1732-69), a French metallurgist, visited Newcastle upon Tyne, and described the engine he saw working at the Walker colliery near by. It had been built by William Brown, a local colliery engineer…The first scientific engineer to devote much attention to steam power was John Smeaton….he also obtained from William Brown a list of about 100 engines in the north of England, with particulars and the performances of 15 of them, having cylinders ranging from 20 to 75 inches in diameter, and collected further particulars of 18 large engines in Cornwall.

"From the data, he found that on the average they raised the equivalent of 5.59 m lb of water one foot high for the consumption of one bushel of coal….The average effective pressure on the pistons was only 6.72 lb to the sq in…which was no better than Newcomen had obtained…Smeaton, with knowledge and manufacturing facilities unavailable to Newcomen, almost doubled the efficiency of the atmospheric steam engine, raising its performance about as high as was possible with this type."

The world's first engine spotter, William Brown, had gathered the data needed for scientific analysis and aided, in his time, the doubling of heat engine efficiency.

The point of this is to understand that evolution alone will not always yield the best results, although some would argue that the development of science in itself is evolutionary. My reference is, however, to the evolution of the steam engine. In the first practical applications of steam to useful motion, the steam was contained close to atmospheric pressure, inducing movement by virtue of condensation, put simply, by steam turning back to liquid. In condensing, the steam takes up much less space and creates a vacuum. Atmospheric pressure, roughly 15 pounds per square inch (psi), is greater than no pressure and must always win the pushing contest. Pressure is directly related to force and in the imperial system of units it is the number of pounds of force for each square inch of surface subjected to that pressure. Thus force increases with the square of the diameter. 15psi gives about 1150 pounds of force on the piston rod of a 10in diameter piston; 15psi gives about 4700 pounds of force on the piston rod of a 20in diameter piston. Atmospheric pressure is pretty much the same everywhere on the Earth's surface (yes, it does vary, but for the atmospheric steam engine it is as good as constant). In order to increase the force on the piston rod of a fixed pressure, atmospheric, engine, the only recourse is to increase the area of the piston. This was done in the eighteenth century and some huge machines evolved as a result. Rather than getting closer to the mobile locomotive, which needed to be compact, we moved

further away!

Boulton and Watt continued to build these machines well past their "sell by date" in spite of the fact that they were, eventually, woeful compared to others available in their time, in particular high-pressure steam engines.

One could say that the atmospheric trains of I.K. Brunel reputedly got quite a trot on, but the effective stoke of the piston, accelerating constantly due to atmospheric pressure, was the length of the line between station stops, not the distance to produce half a turn of the crank as in the travelling engine. Acceleration of the piston is equal to the force on the piston divided by the mass attached to it. If you accelerate, as in the atmospheric railway, along the whole length of the track, one can eventually be doing a considerable speed, no matter what the mass or force. The highest speed recorded was 70mph with a train of 28 tons. With the relatively small piston and short stroke of a mobile engine, friction, heavy mass reciprocation and movement (that is, large accelerating masses) become much more significant for each of those strokes, and produce forces that are too much for atmospheric engines to cope with. In order to make the steam engine mobile we must look towards higher-pressure steam; that which came to be known as strong steam and later high-pressure steam: steam forced to exceed atmospheric pressure.

Strong Steam

Richard Trevithick was one of the pioneers of mobile steam engines using strong steam in a fire-tube type boiler. In spite of the use of strong steam, Trevithick still had to resort to a massive flywheel to store energy. This was for the effort needed to keep the mobile engine moving while boiler pressure was recovered after the initial start up, which required a lot of steam, just like today's locomotives. But it worked, and a replica still does! The first mobile steam engines worked at about 50psi. The locomotives with conventional multi-tube, fire-tube, boilers with double-skin firebox, ultimately rose to a limit of about 300 to 350psi. To get much past 300psi economically and safely, the large flat-side double-skin firebox had to go. Water tubes provide an answer, where much higher pressures are possible. This was described as extra-high pressure by Gresley and refers to pressures from about 350 to 900psi. Some contemporaries of Gresley tried ultra-high pressure, which generally exceeded 1000psi, during the evolution of the water tube locomotive produced by the Hush-Hush team.

To really understand the need for extra- or ultra-high pressure and compounding, the science of thermodynamics needs to be briefly explored. Thermodynamics (from the Greek *thermos* meaning heat and *dynamics* meaning power) is a branch of physics that studies the effects of changes in temperature, pressure, and volume on physical systems at the macroscopic scale by analysing the collective motion of particles, using statistics. More simply expressed thermodynamics, or heat power, looks at the way heat drives changes. In the case of the steam locomotive, how heat power produces mechanical work. Historically, thermodynamics developed out of the need to increase the efficiency of early steam engines, which are typical thermodynamic systems. Heat moves from hot (boiler) to cold (condenser) and work is extracted (a heat engine).

The laws of thermodynamics postulate that energy can be exchanged between physical systems, heat to work and work to heat. They also postulate the existence of a quantity named entropy, which can be defined for any system and relates to the state of a system. In thermodynamics, interactions between large ensembles of objects, rather than individual atomic particles, are studied and categorised. Central to this are the concepts of *system* and *surroundings*. A system is composed of particles, whose average motions define its properties, which in turn are related to one another through equations of state. Properties can be combined to express internal energy and thermodynamic potentials, which are useful for determining conditions for equilibrium and spontaneous processes. That is, if, in what direction, and how fast a system will work. With these tools, thermodynamics describes how systems respond to changes in their surroundings. This can be applied to a wide variety of topics in science and engineering, such as engines, phase transitions, chemical reactions, transport phenomena, and even black holes. Today it has been realised that the laws of thermodynamics are the fundamental laws upon which all other laws depend. In the time of Gresley however, the understanding of thermodynamics was in its relative infancy and engineers were groping for answers, trying to make sense of experimental data, often unable to see the wood for the trees, rather than the more ordered and systematic view of today. Most of them got their compound steam systems analysis quite wrong.

In thermodynamics there are four laws of very general validity, and they do not depend on the details of the interactions or the systems being studied. Hence, they can be applied to systems about which one knows nothing other than the balance of energy and matter transfer. Examples of this include Einstein's prediction of spontaneous emission from around the turn of the 20th century and current research into the thermodynamics of black holes. For us it is the steam locomotive.

The Zeroth law of thermodynamics states that thermodynamic equilibrium is an equivalence relationship. If two thermodynamic systems are separately in thermal equilibrium with a third, they are also in thermal equilibrium with each other. This is intuitively obvious, but it might not have been the case, and must be stated. Temperature controls heat transfer, not the total heat in an object. The existence of this law allows thermometers to work. This law was in its infancy in the first third of the 20th century.

The first law of thermodynamics, about the conservation of energy, states that the change in the internal energy of a closed thermodynamic system is equal to the sum of the amount of heat energy supplied to the system and the work done on the system. Put simply, energy can neither be created or destroyed, heat to work or work to heat. Without this law comparisons could not be made to show the merits of one system over another.

The second law of thermodynamics, about entropy, states that the total entropy of any isolated thermodynamic system tends to increase over time, approaching a maximum value. This is the law that caused the confusion and in Gresley's time and is described as "a measure of disorder in a system". We now know that it is related to potentials and ordered states and how heat in a system behaves as temperature increases. I suspect however that the eventual design choice of 450psi for 10000 and eventually 475psi in practice suggests that he had a good idea about the relationship between entropy and system state as approximately 400 to 500psi is one of the maxima for British Thermal Unit (btu) per pound of steam.

The third law of thermodynamics, about absolute zero temperature, states that as a system asymptotically approaches absolute zero temperature, all processes virtually cease and the entropy of the system asymptotically approaches a minimum value; this can also be stated as: "the entropy of a perfectly crystalline body at absolute zero temperature is zero". It is impossible to reach absolute zero, heat flows from a hot body to a colder one and therefore to become colder something has to be colder still. There is nothing colder than absolute zero therefore absolute zero is out of reach.

The Combined Law incorporates all of the above into one mathematical statement

The Search for Efficiency

Work Done and Efficiency

The study of thermodynamics changes pure intuition followed by observation and measurement into scientific law. It becomes clearer, if one understands the laws, that there is a limit to the amount of work done for a given amount of heat. This can be measured and is called the mechanical equivalent of heat. The work done by a locomotive, therefore, is limited by the device that turns the heat, in the steam, into work; the work manifesting itself in the form of a train in motion. The mechanism that does this is simply piston and cylinder. Heat is admitted into the cylinder in front of the piston, in the form of steam, water moving at very high speed and therefore very hot. The steam moves, expands and slows down driving the piston, atmospheric pressure and exhaust steam, on the back of the piston, cooling in the process. Thus heat is turned into work by moving the piston and everything attached to it.

This is in reality just another form of transfer of momentum. The momentum of the steam, in the steam engine, transfers to the piston and makes it move. The way we quantify momentum in steam is with a thermometer, temperature being a measure of the momentum of something hot, and this is read, in the case of steam, when the heat exchange from steam to thermometer has ceased and they are in equilibrium as explained by the Zeroth law; for this to be possible, the heat engine needs to be in a steady state. From this it becomes clear that the cylinder does it all. The remaining machine exists purely to serve the cylinders. No wonder that the engineers who truly understood thermodynamics began concentrating upon cylinder events and produced continuous expansion and multiple-stage, compound steam engines.

We have stated that the momentum of the steam is quantified by temperature and therefore it is the temperature that gives us a measure of how well the cylinders convert the momentum of the steam into motion. Assuming negligible heat loss from the cylinder wall, thermodynamic efficiency is as follows:

$$\frac{T\ in\ -\ T\ out}{T\ in} \times 100\%$$

Intuition will tell you this if you think about the mechanical equivalent of heat. Heat is turned to work and the higher the drop in temperature through the cylinder, the more heat has been turned into work. Minimising loss to the surroundings is where good cylinder design comes into play. This is not the actual efficiency of the machine but the maximum theoretically possible with the temperatures achieved, and in this case theory is far from reality. To be 100 percent efficient, all of the energy in the steam has to be converted to work, which is impossible on Earth. To get below surrounding ambient temperatures, the locomotive would also need to be a refrigerator. Note that a highly significant proportion of the heat was already in the water, sitting in the water tower or trough. This was conveniently forgotten by the anti-steam lobby and those who were against compounding. The true efficiency of the machine is much greater. This is why Gresley was so anxious to have a testing station to produce the steady state necessary to compare one form of motive power with another under controlled conditions, quite impossible on the open road. For example, an increase from 8% efficient to 16%, typical of compounds, gives an improvement of 100%! Temperatures in to and out of the cylinders give the start and finish points for the efficiency of the machine, and once we have made the difference in temperatures as high as is practically possible, the maximum efficiency of the machine, as a whole, is fixed.

In respect to the above we should also know that the higher the pressure, the higher the temperature, steam or water, and for dry steam:

P represents pressure
V represents volume
M represents mass
r represents the universal gas constant
T represents the temperature

```
P x V = M x r x T
```
Work = Heat

It is true that the efficiency with which the heat is transferred from the boiler to the heat engine (that is, the cylinders) has significant importance in the *overall* thermal efficiency of the machine, as well as cylinder heat loss and what happens after the heat engine (motion, wheels etc). As with "diesels and electrics" these issues must be dealt with separately to have any value at all. Indeed the main thrust of the Hush-Hush project was to produce a boiler of higher thermal efficiency. To take advantage of the higher pressure, Gresley considered that they must do something meaningful with the cylinders, that is, move to continuous expansion offered by two or more stages of expansion. Note that the efficiency relationship to temperature includes pressure and thus superheating does not help in this respect as it is at constant pressure; it only has a secondary effect at best.

A Two-Stage Compound

An ideal cylinder and piston would increase in diameter along the length of it to compensate for the pressure drop during expansion of the steam. One of the compound designs did, sort of, have an expanding piston and cylinder! Tandem compounds were a fair approximation, using one piston rod for two tandem cylinders, one high pressure and one larger-diameter low pressure. The cylinders are not truly separate but are a single cylinder made longer by virtue of splitting it into two halves, each half separately driving the locomotive cranks. The exhaust steam from the first half is fed to the second half, by now at a reduced pressure. The second half must therefore be of a larger diameter to give the same force on the piston rod. Hence we have a small-diameter, high-pressure, half cylinder and a large-diameter, low-pressure, other half. Not only do we have a cylinder much nearer the ideal, stepping up in size along its length, but the steam now has twice as far to go per revolution in order to squeeze out every bit of energy possible. Remember the atmospheric railway accelerating along the length of the line? We will have more to say on this later.

Herbert Nigel Gresley

The Baby, Child and Adolescent

In 1876 Mrs Gresley, made the trip from Netherseal to Edinburgh to have her next child. She had lost the previous two children, early, and it was thought prudent to get the best available assistance this time around. On 19th June 1876, Herbert Nigel Gresley thus spent his first hours to the echoes of the North Eastern, North British, Caledonian and Midland whistles.

Mrs Gresley and son soon returned to Netherseal, near Swadlincote, Derbyshire and Nigel began his early childhood in Midland territory, close to the church, Nigel's father being rector at Netherseal. Gresley inevitably experienced the nearby LNW and Midland railways during these early years, and an information board at Netherseal suggests that he probably gained his interest in locomotives whilst observing them at the nearby colliery.

The rural village, idyllic and quiet even in 2010, would have limited excitement for a young lad, and the trains must have been particularly enthralling in those circumstances. The railway network on the British mainland was growing at a rate of about two hundred miles per year by the time he went to prep school.

Nigel's prep school was some distance from Netherseal, at St Leonards, Hastings, Sussex where the London Brighton and South Coast met the South Eastern and Chatham. By the end of his days at St Leonards the railway network on the British mainland had risen to about seventeen and a half thousand miles.

Later, in 1890, the adolescent Nigel was to attend Marlborough College, near Swindon, where of course the Great Western dominated (and still two years before the demise of the broad gauge). Nigel completed his school education at Marlborough College, one of the Masters being the father of Edward Thompson. The relationship between Nigel and Edward, in later days, must have been influenced by this; however they were not at school together, Edward attending Marlborough after Nigel's departure. During his time there, Gresley traced a Great Northern Stirling Single and was technically very proficient by all accounts. During the years from the start of Gresley's stay at Marlborough to the start of his days as premium apprentice, the railway network on the British mainland had risen to eighteen thousand miles.

The Apprentice

Gresley was finally apprenticed in June 1894 as premium pupil of Francis Webb at the Crewe locomotive works of the London & North Western Railway, aged 17 years. During his stay, he experienced the construction of: 2-4-2T Simple, 0-6-0 Simple Cauliflower, 0-6-2T Simple Coal Tank, 2-4-0 Simple 150psi improved Precedent, 2-4-0 Simple 150psi Waterloo, 2-2-2-2 Compound 175psi Greater Britain, 0-8-0 Compound, 0-4-2WT Simple Crane, 2-2-2-2 Compound 175psi John Hick, 0-4-2ST Simple (more like pannier) and 4-4-0 Compound 200psi Jubilee locomotives, as well as the rebuild and maintenance of many others, including Lady of the Lake Singles.

All this occurred during his formative years when influences are at their strongest. The Preston crash on the 13th July 1896 that put an end to the famous races to the North must have influenced his approach to express steam working. Gresley was always an advocate of increasing speed uphill to reduce timings, rather than go for excessive speed downhill. Modest increases in speed uphill have potential for much greater savings in time than increases in speeding down. With this in mind, why did Gresley go on to produce the fastest steam locomotive of all time? What influence caused him to do this in complete opposition to his strongly held belief?

The LNWR dynamometer car for road testing was in use during Gresley's apprenticeship and this is when Gresley would have realised that a testing station was

Sent to the Chicago Exhibition in 1893 where it gained the gold medal for excellence of workmanship and subsequently ran a L. & N W. train from Chicago to New York, the only British train ever run in America. Specially painted white and with the Royal Arms in honor of Queen Victoria's Diamond Jubilee in 1897 Has run 473,759 miles to end of Sept. 1904.

COMPOUND PASSENGER ENGINE "QUEEN EMPRESS". BUILT 1893. DRIVING WHEELS 7 FT. DIAMETER.

Queen Empress. A favourite of Gresley's, he often talked of this fine machine. It was brand new when he was a premium apprentice at Crewe. It had a mid-combustion chamber, effectively making the front section of the boiler a pre-heater. (Author's Collection)

required, at an early stage in his career. (How frustrating must his work in the remaining years have been; he died before his station was completed.)

Two other developments from this time were to have an influence on Gresley. 1502 *Black Prince* was fitted with a double chimney. Each chimney was partitioned, one drawing from the upper tubes and the other from the lower. A favourite of Gresley's was 2-2-2-2 compound *Queen Empress,* which had a mid combustion chamber in the barrel quite separate from the firebox, to allow the larger of the burning carry-over ashes to fall out and burn to completion. The front section of the barrel was then, to all intents and purposes, a pre-heater with only very fine ash and gasses being driven through to the smokebox. There was a valve to allow the ashes in the mid combustion chamber to fall out. The front barrel section as a pre-heater was to be adopted by André Chapelon in his 160A1 experimental locomotive, the power of which staggered the locomotive world. Photographs and further information regarding the LNWR locomotives

in this period can be found in *The Premier Line* by O.S. Nock.

Water-Tube Locomotives at Crewe at That Time

Isaac Watt Boulton had bought redundant Sturrock powered tenders and rebuilt them into locomotives with water-tube boilers (cross water tubes in a circular flue). These gave satisfaction and Boulton, in attempting to get Webb to hire one for trial, at least succeeded in getting him to try it for himself. Webb produced two locomotives in 1875 with water-tube boilers. Note that they had triple blast pipes and chimneys!

These locomotives almost certainly gave the young Gresley his first encounter with successful water-tube boilers. One of these was to last into 1930. *The Chronicles of Boulton's Siding* by Alfred Rosling Bennett reveals the details of Boulton's water-tube locomotives.

After completing his formal apprenticeship, aged 21 years, Gresley remained at Crewe for a further year,

Billy. *The first water-tube boiler that Gresley experienced must have been Billy (or Dickie). Built in 1875 and still at work in 1930, it had cross water tubes in the boiler with triple blast pipe and chimney. (LNWR Society)*

working as a fitter to gain practical experience. The new 4-4-0 compound 200psi Jubilee class had become the "state of the art" on the LNWR at that time. Notice the increase in boiler pressure from 150psi to 200psi during his short five-year stay. It is hardly surprising that Webb needed his compounds; simple design would have been hard pressed to keep up with such a leap. This was a precursor to Gresley's even bigger jump a quarter of a century later.

In the years of Gresley's stay at Crewe, the railway network on the British mainland had risen to about nineteen thousand miles and Crewe works was at its most productive ever, in terms of locomotive numbers turned out.

The Journeyman

In 1898 Gresley joined the Lancashire and Yorkshire under John Aspinall. He was in the Horwich drawing office, before going on to material testing in 1899. Aspinall tried his smokebox superheater in 1899, a bank of tubes in the smokebox of Highflyer 4-4-2 No 737. This was the same arrangement as the boiler of the LNWR 2-2-2-2, but the front pre-heater section was replaced by a set of tubes drying the steam rather than pre-heating the water. Mr Gresley became Blackpool shed foreman in 1899 at the age of 23. The Highfliers on which heated jackets were applied to the cylinders in an attempt to improve cylinder efficiency were to be seen at Blackpool. I have no doubt that Gresley took more than a passing interest in the tests and their outcome.

Aspinall converted Flyer 4-4-0 No 1112 into a 4-cylinder compound with LNWR type cab/splashers in September 1901. Druitt-Halpin thermal storage cylinders began to be installed on some machines, the first in June 1902. The cylinders of the system were mounted on top of the boiler and, I understand, gave some advantage on rising gradients but not enough to continue the practice.

One highly significant occurrence on the L&Y during Gresley's stay involved 0-8-0 No 676, built July 1900. This was involved in a fatal boiler explosion while passing east of Knottingley. In response to this 0-8-0 No 392 had a new design of boiler fitted. This incorporated a cylindrical corrugated steel firebox. This was a variation of the fireboxes produced to the designs of Jacobs-Schubert, Lentz and Vanderbilt in mainland Europe and the USA. It was successful enough for another twenty to be built with this boiler in 1903. The boilers lasted for about ten years. After living at Newton Heath for a period, Gresley then moved to the Great Northern in 1905.

The Engineer

In 1905, aged 29, Gresley became Great Northern Railway Carriage and Wagon Superintendent, and by now there were twenty thousand miles of railways on the British mainland. From 1905 to 1911 Gresley remained Carriage and Wagon Superintendent and during these years compounding took a beating. Francis William Webb (1842-1906) and Walter Mackersie Smith (1836-1906), the two central figures, died in the same year. Webb with highly successful compounds, eventually, on the LNWR, and Smith, successful from the start it seems, on the NER. Compared to these men, other railway engineers invested in compounding only on a small scale.

O.S. Nock tells us of the "notable paper by Hughes" (George Hughes 1860-1945 L&Y chief engineer 1904-1921, LNWR 1922 and LMS 1923-1925). In his paper, read to the Institution of Mechanical Engineers in 1910:

"The author reasons that very little benefit will accrue from compounding express passenger engines. The value of compounding largely depends on the reduction of the range of temperatures in the cylinders. High piston speeds reduce this range in express work even with early cut off, and these conditions do not exist in slow running goods engines"

The NER was not represented to dispute this and I suspect that the appointment to engineering chief of Vincent Raven in this very year precluded involvement in a potentially highly-charged debate. Nock points out that Bowen Cooke, Churchward, Earle Marsh, Fowler and Aspinall were all in attendance. Unfortunately any reasoning with regard to compounding was flawed due to the way in which compounds were believed to work at their optimum. This will be discussed later.

William Guy Granet

Granet was born on 13th October 1867 and educated at Rugby and Balliol College, becoming a barrister in 1893. He married the daughter of the Speaker of the House of Commons in 1892. He became Secretary of the Railway Companies' Association in 1900, Assistant to the General Manager of the Midland Railway in 1905 and it's General Manager in 1906. His interests included traffic control and industrial relations (he was secretary to the Employers' Committee during the general railway strike of 1907). He joined the Board of the Midland Railway in 1918 and became its Chairman in 1922. Rutherford notes that "Granet was undoubtedly one of those who wished to reduce the status, power (and salaries) of the idiosyncratic Victorian locomotive superintendents."

He may well have arrived at that view (or received it from others and promulgated it further) whilst he was Secretary of the Railway Companies' Association. Certainly, once Granet became General Manager of the Midland Railway, R.M. Deeley's attempts to introduce appropriate modern locomotive power, eight-coupled engines for freight and four-cylinder de Glehn compound 4-6-0s for "crack" expresses, got nowhere and Deeley left in 1909. Deeley was replaced by Henry Fowler who was a man of wide interests, but not the design of locomotives, although he was interested in details such as the application of superheating or the metallurgy of boiler stays. The concept of "the dead hand of Derby" in locomotive matters (and other British railway workshops come to that), can be traced back to these events. Ironically, in 1924, the LMS was to proliferate the Midland copies of the NER Smith compounds, with some differences, with George Hughes in charge. All 195 of them survived into the British Railways era along with the 45 previously introduced by the Midland in 1902 by Johnson and finished in 1905 by Deeley. The LMS was to be consulted in respect to 10000, but they thought it was to do with compounding of D49s!

Granet resigned in October 1927 and moved to the City. *Fury*, the Royal Scot built as an ultra-high-pressure boiler compound was briefly introduced in 1929 at more or less the same time as 10000.

By 1911, aged 35, Gresley was Chief Mechanical Engineer, GNR, based at Kings Cross. In his early years in the post he continued to build some of Ivatt's designs: C1 4-4-2 and J6 0-6-0. He then went on to build his own K1 2-6-0, K2 2-6-0, J50 0-6-0T, N2 0-6-2T, O1 2-8-0 and O2 2-8-0. Gresley worked with Churchward, Hughes and Fowler in connection with Association of Railway Locomotive Engineers' proposals for new British Standard designs towards the end of WWI. At the age of 44, in 1920, he was awarded the CBE. Gresley continued with his K3 2-6-0 and A1 4-6-2. In 1923 the LNER was formed and, at the age of 47, the post of Chief Mechanical Engineer LNER was his. The A5 4-6-2T, P1 2-8-2, U1 2-8-0+0-8-2T and, from Sentinel, Y1 0-4-0T all followed.

Developments with Cylinders

We have dealt with the background theory relating to the need to increase the temperature range across the cylinders in order to improve the thermal efficiency of reciprocating steam locomotives. It was asserted that, in order to take advantage of the increased pressure, hence temperature, offered by more thermally-efficient extra-high-pressure boilers, something meaningful needed to be done with the cylinders. 10000 had four "engines", each one working on the forward and return stroke giving eight cylinder cycles per revolution of the wheel. However 10000, as a two stage compound, had two cylinders involved in any one cycle and, crucially, it was thus a four cycle per revolution machine. Only a few engineers realised the significance of this, and evidence seems to indicate that only Chapelon ever got it right in actual hardware on the Société Nationale des Chemins de fer Français (SNCF).

The overall pressure (thus temperature) range can be increased with a higher pressure boiler, combined with two cylinders serviced from one charge of steam per revolution, as in the case of two-stage expansion, to increase efficiency on two fronts. That is, to reduce heating and cooling effects and gain more expansive use of the steam. Alternatively, the same pressure dissipated over two cylinders with two charges of steam, reducing the wall temperature range in each cylinder, reducing heating and cooling losses, with resultant efficiency gain. This can be achieved by admitting steam through a different port to the one that exhausts, as in uniflow or poppet valves. This only gives a single benefit. Gresley chose compounding.

The Great Northern had a look at compounds.

Ivatt's first compound GN Atlantic was produced in 1905. It had four cylinders, two inside low-pressure cylinders driving the leading coupled axle with Stephenson valve gear, and two outside high-pressure cylinders driving the second coupled axle with Walschaerts gear. It lasted this way for its lifetime of 23 years. Great Northern compound 1300 was the second of their experimental four-cylinder compounds, purchased from the Vulcan Foundry after enquiries to them, and other manufacturers, by the board. The third and final Great Northern compound, No 1421, was a four-cylinder machine much the same as their first but with enlarged inside cylinders.

The North Eastern Railway produced the first Smith three-cylinder compound, which also had cross water tubes. The first NER Uniflow locomotive was No 825. Sir Vincent Raven is on record as saying that it "gave satisfaction" and he was sufficiently encouraged to build a Z-class Atlantic with three Uniflow cylinders in 1919. It was 2½ tons heavier than the conventional Z-class Atlantics, and much of the extra load had to be taken by the front bogie. It was used on prestige routes; however in 1934 it was converted to Lentz poppet valves and was finally taken out of use in October 1945.

The misconception with compounds related to cut off. In a simple, single-stage, cylinder the steam is only admitted for a proportion of the piston stroke. How far along the cylinder depends upon the demand for force. On starting, the required force is at a maximum and, uniquely to the steam engine, this is when the maximum force is available. It is achieved by allowing full boiler pressure, as far as is attainable, for most of the piston stroke. After the train achieves the required velocity (speed in a straight line) the force needed to maintain it is significantly reduced, most of the force is needed only to accelerate the train to the desired velocity (which includes going up hill at constant velocity) the remainder is to overcome resistance such as sticktion (I mean friction, but I like that word, it says it so well). The force is reduced by allowing only a small amount of steam into the cylinder, cutting off the flow (cut off) earlier in the stroke of the piston, using the gears (reverser). In both cases (simple and compound) the pressure drops rapidly, reducing the average force over the length of the cylinder, the average being lower with an early cut off.

It all comes down to systems analysis. If each cylinder is considered as an individual system, experience would suggest that as early a cut off as possible should be used in normal running. Most engineers working with continuous expansion, including Hughes in 1910, did this, and were wrong. In a two-stage compounded arrangement, the high pressure and low pressure form a cylinder set and must be analysed as one system. The result is startlingly different; it works, and Chapelon proved it.

To determine cut offs with continuous, say, two-stage expansion, we must look at the volume of the cylinder swept by the piston, not simply the stroke, as it is the volume of steam that is doing the work and the two cylinders must be seen as one, in two steps. This means that the high pressure, first, stage will be at full boiler pressure for most of its stroke, no matter how short the cut off in the equivalent simple expansion cylinder. Even a very early cut off in the equivalent simple expansion cylinder translates as very late in a "high pressure" first stage and only "early" in the second stage.

A two-cylinder (two halves by my argument) two-stage compound is in fact equivalent to a single cylinder simple with the "mechanicals" of a two-cylinder simple. It is potentially efficient enough to be equivalent to a two-cylinder simple, intuition suggesting using half the quantity of steam.

A three-cylinder (three thirds by my argument) three-stage compound is in fact equivalent to a single cylinder simple with the "mechanicals" of a three-cylinder simple. It is potentially efficient enough to be equivalent to a three-cylinder simple, intuitively using one third of the steam.

The trick is to get enough steam, at as high an incoming pressure as possible, to take full advantage of such arrangements whilst leaving enough to exhaust to produce an adequate draught on the fire. This can be done by allowing a full charge of steam in the high-pressure cylinders and adjusting to demand with the remaining stage or stages. The need for compounding with 10000 was undeniable because there was a lot of pressure to work off during one rotation of the wheels. Remember the comment about the relatively short stroke of a mobile machine, made earlier. Using the steam over a full rotation, with a two-stage compound, has to be better than over half a revolution of the simple engine, but the three-stage compound could be stretching things a bit far for the first prototype.

Gresley went for two stages. The initial three-cylinder concept being half and two quarters (one high pressure and two low, each of the low in series with the high, and parallel to each other). This was equivalent to a single cylinder simple! The production version ended up with four cylinders (two high-pressure cylinders in parallel, in series with two low-pressure cylinders, in parallel). In the period in which the machine was "four cylinders equal", 10000 was, intuitively, thermally equivalent to a two cylinder simple machine with the *potential* tractive effort of a four. In the period in which the machine was "pseudo three cylinder", 10000 was, intuitively, thermally equivalent to a single cylinder simple machine with the *potential* tractive effort of a three.

Compounding was commonplace at the inception of 10000. Some notable examples are du Bousquet's Baltic, Edouard Sauvage's three cylinder compound set at the ideal LP 90deg to LP both 135 deg to HP, Mallet's two cylinder compound, Karl Gölsdorf's unmistakable work, the Johnstone annular compound, the von Borries two-cylinder compound, Baldwin Vauclain Compound with the outside cylinder sets, one high-pressure below, one low-pressure above, sharing a common crosshead. The Hungarian 2-6-6-0 Compound Mallet had a Brotan-Deffner water-tube boiler and 58 of these were built over 37 years between 1914 and 1951! The de Glehn four-cylinder compound had spread to the USA. Then there were tandem compounds, mentioned earlier, with high- and low-pressure cylinders in line driving a common piston rod. The du Bousquet tandem for the French Nord and the Santa Fe tandems were, at the time, the most powerful locomotives in the world. We also had the Worsdell von Borries Smith Compound Locomotives for the North Eastern Railway, which evolved into the Midland compound 4-4-0 and Smith NER compound Atlantic. These and others are described and illustrated in *Compound Locomotives* by J.T. van Riemsdijk.

The Collective

Nothing to do with the Borg! Well, possibly, in some ways. I talk of the origins of the final ideas that came together in "Hush-Hush". How on earth did Gresley get directly from the A1 Pacific to the spaceship that was 10000? This evolved on the drawing board and in the workshop in the same way as locomotives of today. Of course, the same steps would take a few days with today's CAD-CAM rather than the years it took on paper, ink on film, and with physical templates and full size experimentation. Was this a dramatic and brave experiment? Well maybe not. The London and North Eastern Railway was going through tough times and needed to save money. There were no resources to apply to electrification, or refurbishment of existing stock, at the time; in fact the Shildon to Newport line was to revert to steam in the near future. There were no railway races as these had come to an abrupt end, quite a way back, with the crash on the

LNWR when Gresley was an apprentice on that railway; therefore there was no demand upon increased speed. The need was for more economy from the existing and immediately-planned work. The financiers would listen to anyone offering bigger profit margins, or any profit at all, due to technical economies that they might not quite understand. Desperate times lead to desperate measures. Coal had become a precious and costly resource for more reasons than one.

Developments throughout the Northern Hemisphere showed the way forward. International Railway Congress meetings allowed for mutual exchange of ideas. Gresley was primarily concerned with improving boiler efficiency at this time and had quite some experience acquired in his own lifetime; in addition he also had some other influential and successful precursors providing the where-with-all, and they go a surprising way back.

Water-Tube Boilers

Amongst other things, we have discussed early railways up to Trevithick, but now we must take a different road to that of conventional railway locomotive history, a parallel path if you like. Water tubes take in heat at a high rate and will flash off steam to provide instant power, relatively speaking. The first time that this applied to the travelling railroad locomotive that I have come across was Timothy Hackworth's "Globe" with cross water tubes. What a machine; fast as the wind it seems, probably too fast for the line in fact. Eventually the water tubes were taken out, making the locomotive conventional. Sadly, in this conventional state she blew up! How is it that he built those hulking great dinosaurs, which admittedly did the job, and amongst them "Globe"? A drawing of Globe can be found on Mr Hackworth's business card and it is also interesting to note a reference to "marine engineer" on the same card. The original printing plate for this business card and a Globe stamp can be seen at the National Railway Museum at Locomotion, Shildon.

Drummond's cross-water-tube fireboxes, introduced in 1897, remained standard until he died in 1912. There was the cross-tube boiler fitted to his K10 4-4-0 tender engine No 343. How the cross tubes in the barrel were kept clear of scale, I don't know. Likewise I know nothing of the performance it gave. This locomotive is illustrated and described in *The LSWR at Nine Elms* by Barry Curl.

In the USA, the North Pacific Coast Locomotive No 21 is of note. This was an experiment in locomotive design by Bill Thomas, chief engineer of the NPC circa

1900. It was an oil-fired cab-forward design with a marine-type water-tube boiler, and carried a horizontal steam drum above the boiler. The boiler consisted of a long corrugated firebox/flue, similar to the L&Y 0-8-0 firebox mentioned on page 9, with longitudinal water tubes at the top. In the steam drum was a lower, perforated, pipe for boiler feed, and an upper, perforated, pipe for steam collection. From the drum, the steam passed through a regulator valve and then to the cylinders via two vertical pipes in the cab. Exhaust was carried to the rear and to a conventional blast pipe.

Extra-High-Pressure Boilers

One type in particular became the forerunner of a whole variety of developments, including 10000. The Brotan boiler was devised by Johann Brotan, who was chief of the Gmünd Workshop of the Austrian StEG, the State Railway Company. He patented it in 1902, and it was widely used in Hungary, but much less so in other countries. The distinguishing features of the Brotan was its water-tube firebox attached to a conventional fire-tube barrel, which, like the Flaman boiler, held water and communicated with a cylindrical steam reservoir above both of them. The spaces between the water-tube firebox and fire-tube barrel were filled with firebrick. They were popular with the Hungarian State Railway, MÁV, because the boiler construction did not require copper and Hungary had little in the way of copper reserves. Hungary, like most European railways, did not adopt the American practice of making the firebox from sheet steel. It is of note that many of the Hungarian Brotan locomotives survived until the end of the steam era. Other centres followed suit, some with straightforward Brotans, but several with patent-avoiding variations.

Mr Deffner, also an Austrian railway mechanist, developed a modified version of the Brotan boiler, the Brotan-Deffner. The Deffner design kept the fire-tube barrel, as in the original, but substituted a steam reservoir for the steam drum; it connected and merged into both the fire-tube barrel and the water-tube firebox. The all-steel firebox with the dual-row tube wall remained as before. This increased the boiler height; the boiler lagging became simpler and thus resulted in the conical shape so familiar with this type of boiler. The huge Brotan boiler of the Class 601 Mallet 2-6-6-0 had two steam reservoirs in parallel, instead of one, a feature to be repeated in the USA. The all-steel Brotan boilers were particularly in favour during WWI, when limited copper resources were badly needed by the armaments industry. The firebricks of the firebox front often failed. To overcome this, Mr Mihály Kubinszky, the MÁV chief engineer, designed a steel front wall in the 1920s, and this was applied to some locomotives.

An extract from a paper by Dipl-Ing Gaspar Szontagh (Transactions of The Newcomen Society: *Brotan and Brotan-Deffner Type Fireboxes and Boilers applied to Steam Locomotives*. Vol. 62, 1990-91, pages 21-51) states:

"The construction of the Brotan water tube boiler is well known. The side walls of the firebox are replaced by large water tubes. The upper ends of these tubes are fixed in one or two drums communicating with the barrel. The lower ends are fastened into a hollow foundation ring. This is also connected at the barrel. In this way free circulation of the water in the firebox tubes is assured. The barrel is of the orthodox type, excepting that the firebox tubeplate is circular like the smokebox tubeplate.

"The Brotan boiler is well designed and steams freely on account of the water tube firebox; the steam produced, however, is wetter than in an ordinary boiler. The efficiency of the boiler is good and from tests carried out by the Polish State Railways the consumption of fuel in a Brotan boiler is about 5% less than in a boiler of orthodox type.

"Compared with the ordinary firebox the junction between the foundation ring and the barrel is less rigid and contains a certain number of parts where the metal is affected by alternating stresses caused by expansion and by vibration, which causes fatigue of the material. The cracks which develop at these places make it necessary to replace the parts in question after a relatively short time. It is also difficult to keep the water tubes permanently tight in the steam drums.

"The defects are for the most part developed:

a) in the corners of the lower part of the firebox tubeplate
b) around the openings in the firebox tubeplate which are riveted to the steam drum
c) in the water tubes
d) on the circumference of the steam drum.

"Leakage is apt to develop at the following points:

a) rivets around firebox tubeplate
b) rivets between steam drum and the boiler barrel
c) where the water tubes enter the steam drum

d) connections between the foundation ring and the barrel.

"The water tubes of the Brotan boiler require frequent descaling, especially where the feed water is not good, and this requires special descaling tools."

Clearly Gresley had been aware of these defective areas and in one move eliminated the lot. The barrel was not necessary and could easily be replaced by alternative pre-heating arrangements. (I am at a loss as to why André Chapelon suggested the Brotan-Deffner for future steam when that produced for 10000, without the troublesome barrel, was so successful.)

The locomotive engineer E. Noltein of the Moscow-Kazan Railway was an early supporter of water-tube fireboxes and began experiments in the late 1890s. The appearance of the Brotan water-tube boiler prompted him to advocate fitting Brotan fireboxes to a number of locomotives as a trial. Construction of two experimental boilers for 0-8-0 goods locomotives began in 1904. One was fitted to locomotive AH No 447. After two years of trials Noltein claimed lower repair costs, which met his main aim, and fuel savings of 14.8%. A Belgian locomotive, No 2804, originally built at La Meuse in 1900, was rebuilt with a Brotan boiler in 1908. A few Brotan boilered locomotives survived until the end of the steam era and into preservation.

In 1904, du Bousquet began a project to test water-tube boilers on the French Nord network. The motivation was reportedly a desire to reduce the high maintenance costs of existing conventional boilers and fireboxes, rather than a drive for performance or economy. At first a du Temple marine type was proposed, but the general form of it proved impossible to adapt to locomotive applications. It was therefore decided to adopt a water-tube firebox combined with a conventional cylindrical fire-tube boiler. In this it resembled the Brotan-Deffner boiler. In December 1905 the first boiler was ordered from the Creusot works. Trials were concluded in 1907. The bottom steam drums were of cast steel, protected from the direct heat of the fire by firebricks. There were leaks where the tubes joined the rear tube-plate, caused by a lack of rigidity. However, *The Engineer*, 4 Nov 1910 said:

"But the most important leakage arose from the unequal temperatures between the top and bottom of the boiler. To ensure that the water passing into the water tubes should be as free from deposit as possible, the makers had placed, high up on the boiler barrel, the pipes, which connected the boiler with the collectors. This caused violent differences of temperature, owing to imperfect circulation, until the boiler was producing steam for the cylinders."

Despite this, the first water-tube boiler was said to have been "a successful and economical steam generator". A second, modified boiler was ordered from the Creusot works in 1908. This version built on the lessons of the first; it had no firebricks and a vertical array of water tubes protected the rear tube plate of the boiler from direct flame. The firebox was joined much more rigidly to the boiler barrel than the first one. The heating surface was about 1000 sq ft with a grate area of 37 sq ft; figures that were thought to be unprecedented at the time. After the engine had run over 20,000 miles in normal service, it was said: "... so far no wear can be observed on any of the water tubes, while there is no perceptible amount of sediment deposited in any part of the boiler."

There were amazing examples of intermediate, freight and express passenger Brotans. Some spectacular examples of Brotan boilers were constructed in the United States. These formed the basis of the boiler built by Gresley.

Yarrow had been consultant to the Baltimore and Ohio Railway in connection with the water-tube locomotive fleet and this influenced Gresley in building up a partnership resulting in the joint patent of the boiler for 10000. Examples of the fleet spanning a decade in building can be found in *B&O Power* by Lawrence W. Sagle. The Baltimore and Ohio's first water-tube locomotive was built in 1927 and a photograph shows her at Dover, Ohio in 1948, still at work.

The second, again in 1927, was a Mikado originally built in 1911 and retrospectively fitted with a water-tube boiler. This was exhibited at The Fair of the Iron Horse in Baltimore in 1927. The patents must have been well in place by this event as the inner workings of the firebox were there for all to see. Again it had a water-tube firebox and conventional barrel. I see reflections of the French Nord "Super Pacific" and the reason that Gresley could eliminate the barrel altogether.

Pacific *President Cleveland* was built new in 1928 with the exception of the boiler barrel and tubes, which

1402 James Archbald. *The third of the Delaware & Hudson water-tube locomotives. The top of the boiler was a little more square than 10000 because it has two top drums as opposed to one. (Author's Collection)*

came from Mikado No 4201.

4-8-2 No 5510 and No 5550 were built by Baldwin for the B&O in 1930 in order to further compare the merits of water-tube and conventional boilers, both identical other than the boilers. We get a hint here of what Gresley expected when proposing 10000: an A1, with water-tube boiler and compound, but otherwise identical.

2-6-6-2 No 7400 and No 7450 similarly were produced for direct comparison, again identical in all respects but the fireboxes. The water-tube firebox seems larger than the stayed equivalent. Don't be deceived however; the American had a huge combustion chamber taking up a good deal of the front of the box. Gresley kept the grate area of 10000 down to only 75% of that of the equivalent stayed A1.

John Muhlfeld had been working with the B&O whilst these locomotives were around and he subsequently went on to become consultant to the Delaware and Hudson Railroad, which produced a series of four extra-high-pressure locomotives. For full details of all four, plus several other locomotives mentioned in this book and many other amazing locomotives, visit Douglas Self's website at www.dself.dsl.pipex.com. A paper on the subject, presented by Gresley to the Institution of Mechanical Engineers in January 1931, and referred to later in this book, is still available.

The 60000th product of Baldwin, USA, was No 60000, a 4-10-2 compound drive with water-tube firebox. Like the Brotan-Deffner, the water tube firebox is attached to a conventional fire tube barrel. Thankfully this locomotive can still be seen today in the USA. It is moved several feet, as a demonstration, from time to time.

A report written at the time of the development of 60000 (and 10000) states that:

"1. The locomotive forming the subject of this bulletin is the 60000th locomotive built by The Baldwin Locomotive works. Constructed during the early part of the year 1926 as an experiment to ascertain the possible economies that can be affected by the use of high steam pressures and a high ratio of expansion.

"2. Up to a certain period, development of locomotive design brought with it mainly an increase in weight of individual locomotives, the increase in power being proportionate to the increase in weight. This increase in power made possible notable economies in railroading. Of late years, however, the demand for still further economies has led locomotive designers to strive to increase the efficiency of the locomotive, and thus give increased power per unit of locomotive weight. Among the means adopted to this end, are the use of superheated steam, various fuel and labour saving devices, improved boiler design, more efficient steam distribution and refinements in design and materials for locomotive parts.

"3. At present much thought is being given to the possibility of using higher ratios of expansion to give greater cylinder efficiency and consequently greater horse power per unit of weight.

"4. The great advantage of high pressure steam is that a combination of adequate cylinder force and high ratio of expansion can be obtained with cylinders of moderate dimensions.

"5. In view of the limits set to steam temperatures by the method of producing the steam and by difficulties of lubrication, locomotive designers must, at least for the present, aim at a steam temperature of approximately 650 degrees F., with a maximum of say 700 degrees, irrespective of the pressure used. Now, if the pressure is increased while the temperature remains constant, the superheat and the heat content per pound of steam fall off as the pressure is increased. For example, a steam temperature of 650 degrees F. gives, at 200 pounds per square inch, about 263 degrees superheat and 1340 B.T.U. per pound of steam, and at 350 pounds per square inch about 217 degrees superheat and 1332 B.T.U.

"If steam of 200 pounds per square inch and of 350 pounds per square inch is expanded from the same temperature under such conditions in each case respectively that the exhaust steam escapes at the same pressure and temperature, and with the same heat content in both cases, it follows that the heat taken from the steam in the cylinders and converted into mechanical work will be slightly less with the high than with the low pressure steam. That is, with the same heat content in the exhaust steam, the higher pressure will not give greater thermal efficiency. To reduce the heat content of the exhaust steam and thus increase the thermal efficiency, it is necessary to increase the ratio of expansion.

"6. An increase in the ratio of expansion results in a reduction in the mean effective pressure obtained from a given boiler pressure, and this requires an increase in cylinder dimensions if the same power is to be developed. Now in a large modern locomotive of conventional design, an increase in cylinder dimensions to permit of higher expansion would lead to difficulties in design, and it is advantageous to use a higher boiler pressure so that the increase in expansion can be obtained without involving a loss in power or an abnormal increase in cylinder dimensions.

"7. As a means of obtaining the higher expansion necessary to give economy with steam of 350 pounds per square inch, Locomotive 60,000 was designed with three cylinders compounded, the high-pressure steam being first admitted to the middle cylinder. After expansion there, the steam passes through the receiver in the cylinder saddle to the two outside cylinders where further expansion takes place."

The Sentinels

The story of 10000 includes, naturally, something of Sentinel, as these are water-tube boiler machines, some of which were compounds.

The first Sentinel-like machine was one of three arrangements of water-tube boiler schemed by the 10th Earl of Dundonald. Globe had been built in 1830 at RS&H on behalf of Timothy Hackworth and the S&D Railway with a conventional fire tube and radial cross water tubes, not dramatically different to one of the three scheme diagrams. Access doors to enable inspection of the water tubes were provided. Clearly the danger of furring up of the water tubes was expected, even in these early years. Did the Earl learn this from Mr Hackworth?

Other key features of this locomotive were rotary drive, to eliminate hammer blow, and an exceptionally low centre of gravity, for stability, both desirable characteristics on the long viaduct which was the London and Greenwich Railway, for which it was conceived. Unfortunately, the scheme did not allow for point work or crossings.

An order for the locomotive was placed toward the end of 1835 with John Hague, who also built 0-4-0 No 42 for the S&D Railway. Of note was that T.R. Crampton was engineering trainee with Hague at the time. It is not difficult to make a link between this single wheeler and the famous "Cramptons" to be adopted by French Railways in particular. It is unlikely that the locomotive got beyond initial testing, and it was probably dismantled to make use of the component parts, each of which was individually sound. The failure to get perfectly functioning component parts to successfully work together is a continuing theme to this day.

The drawing office at Crewe had a Sentinel-like locomotive in draft. This was a Beyer Peacock 4-4-0T, of the type well known on the Metropolitan, with triple expansion, using a high-pressure Perkins flash boiler. Schemed at Crewe in the last decade of the 19th century, the triple expansion 3088 "Triplex", which certainly was built and subsequently mentioned in one of Gresley's papers, did not succeed and therefore it is unlikely that the above scheme got beyond the drawing board. Gresley was at Crewe during this period and, if nothing else, it must have been food for thought.

A shunter was built from the power unit of a steam-powered traverser at Doncaster Carriage Works, which was replaced in 1906 when Gresley was Carriage and Wagon Superintendent. The resulting vertical boiler shunter served in the Civil Engineer's yard near Peterborough station from 1908 to 1926. It was painted black with the lettering "GNR", which it kept until it was scrapped. It could almost be described as a Sentinel, which Gresley was to order in number at about the same time as this locomotive was withdrawn!

Thus contemporary with the development of 10000 was the introduction of the Sentinel shunter and Sentinel and Clayton Railcars on the LNER. Most of the railcars had the same boilers as the shunter, that is, vertical with varying sizes and pressures. The Claytons were similar to the Sentinels but offered an alternative supplier, their short life apparently due to the loss of spares when Clayton folded.

A reliable source tells me that Gresley had a financial interest in Sentinel. This may simply be in providing the articulation design for multiple-unit Sentinels, but maybe more than this? The picture of what might have been, with water-tube boilers, becomes significantly greater than a single class of express passenger locomotive and some Sentinels when one LNER and several Sentinel proposals are examined. More of this later.

Ultra-High Pressure Represented by the Schmidt System

The only way to avoid corrosion and scale problems is to use distilled water, as facilitated in power stations. In fact, you need to go further; dissolved gases such as oxygen and carbon dioxide also cause corrosion at high temperatures and pressures, and must be kept out. Generally locomotives did not carry a condenser, so there was no source of pure feed water.

One solution was the Schmidt system. The Schmidt system used a sealed, ultra-high-pressure circuit containing pure, deoxygenated, water that transferred heat by means of coils in a separate high-pressure drum. If the drum is fed with ordinary water, scale might form on the outside of the heating coils, however it cannot cause overheating as the ultra-high-pressure tubes are quite capable of withstanding their internal steam temperature. The high-pressure drum and the ultra-high-pressure water tubes around the firebox were fitted to LMS *Fury*, a Royal Scot with the exception of ultra-high-pressure boiler and compound cylinders, intended to be a direct comparison. The German ultra-high-pressure locomotive H02-1001 was built in 1929.

Why North Road?

Decisions are invariably made with consideration of several factors. The premier works for the LNER during the design and build stages of 10000 is popularly thought to be Doncaster. This may indeed be the case; however the decision was made to use Darlington North Road. Before writing this book I read most, if not all, of the articles written about the subject but never found a satisfactory answer. Disappointingly the file did not give a definitive answer to the question.

History has it that A.C. Stamer, the assistant CME, was based at Stooperdale, Darlington. This alone could have been reason enough. The NER had experience of water tubes in express steam, the GNR had not. The NER had experience of various compounding methods, and in significant numbers. The GNR rebuilt to produce one, built another and had one built for them. The NER had strong links with Crewe, where Gresley had spent his formative years. In fact, the Worsdell brothers, their father and Gresley all worked with F.W. Webb at some time. The NER was forward thinking in its use of new technology, quite literally changing track with electric motive power, whereas the GNR was, in the main, single minded, evolutionary. Raven built a class of large Pacifics that were considered as good as the A1 at Darlington North Road Works. The Stooperdale facility was second to none, and the NER had the dynamometer car.

I suspect it was the legacy of the Worsdells that appealed as much as anything else. The brothers were CMEs in turn and, had their old base, Gateshead, continued with the top link production, 10000 would surely have been constructed there. Due to lack of space at Gateshead, Darlington took over in the first decade of the twentieth century, Darlington had space to grow, and did.

Luckily for Gresley, there was a migration of workers from Gateshead to North Road and the experience gained from contact with the Worsdells went with them. I have a small token of evidence for this. Recently a gentleman dropped off some tools for my workshop with the assertion that "these were my Granddad's, who passed them to my Dad, who passed them to me. Now they are yours". The story goes that the tools started at Gateshead with Granddad, migrated to Darlington with him, passed on to Dad, at

The Crewe Connection				
1851	1857	F.W. Webb	Crewe apprentice	Under Francis Trevithick, son of Richard
1859	1861	F.W. Webb	Crewe chief draughtsman	
c1857	1865	T.W. Worsdell	LNWR	Son of N. Worsdell and trained under John Ramsbottom
1861	1866	F.W. Webb	Crewe works manager	Assistant to John Ramsbottom
1871	1872	T.W. Worsdell	Crewe works manager	
1843	1880	N. Worsdell	LNWR carriages	Son of T.C. Worsdell who built the tender for Rocket L&M
1871	1883	W. Worsdell	LNWR various	Including Crewe
1893	1898	H.N. Gresley	Crewe premium apprentice	To F.W. Webb
1871	1903	F.W. Webb	LNWR locomotive superintendent	Retired in 1903 after 50 years service

HUSH-HUSH – The Story of LNER 10000

Darlington, who then took them to Shildon. Passed to son, at Shildon, to be taken to York and then back to Shildon. Amongst them a small chisel clearly marked "NER G." Magic! It has the usual raggy edges that should have been ground off years ago. They are there for good now, full of history, and in archive. I wonder if it knocked lumps out of 10000?

The Worsdells were at Altoona, Pennsylvania when a substantial combustion chamber, A4-like, was fitted to an American 4-4-0; they saw the first Mogul at work. They were also at Altoona when 2-8-0 locomotives were running. Was this where the T1, T2 and T3s came from? In the USA, 4-6-0s were in use, a quarter of a century before the Highland Railway Jones Goods. The Worsdell brothers were there then.

Down the years large numbers of locomotives were tested using the NER dynamometer car, many of them GWR and LMS types and, of course, 10000. Clearly the NER had the state-of-the-art testing methods and infrastructure, albeit with no rolling road.

As for Stooperdale: "The main entrance, in the centre of the south front, is under an imposing terracotta portico in the Italian style, supported on heavy columns of masonry. The entrance hall is fitted with revolving draught-proof doors."

Local people decided Stooperdale was so splendid that it was Darlington's own Buckingham Palace. "Everything that careful expenditure, architectural skill and good taste could do was done in its construction, and it remains a monument to the princely status of the North Eastern Railway", said a railway historian in 1954. Stooperdale was probably so well appointed – fumed oak woodwork, Terrazzo marble floors –

because it was designed with no lesser person in mind than Sir Vincent Litchfield Raven. He was the chief mechanical engineer of the NER, who lived at Grantly, in Carmel Road (sadly, recently demolished), and came to work every day in either his horse drawn carriage or his chauffeur-driven motor car (from 2nd August 1910, NER employed Albert Cardwell Smith as Raven's private car driver). This may well be why Stooperdale has such an imposing portico entrance – there is nothing a Chief Mechanical Engineer likes less than getting out of his carriage and having to walk a few yards in the rain when a portico could keep him dry.

From his office to the left of the grand entrance, Raven designed and built some 200 locomotives – "all were robust and capable", says the *Oxford Companion to British Railway History* – and made important improvements to signalling. He introduced "automatic train control" between York and Newcastle – a safety device whereby if a train passed a red signal, a bell sounded in the driver's cab and the brake was automatically applied. In 1915, he electrified the Newport to Shildon mineral line and, after WWI, he proposed the electrification of the York to Newcastle main line – clearly a man ahead of his time. A boiler shop and paint shop were built on the Stooperdale estate to augment North Road.

No better examples serve to show the simple evolutionary path taken by the Great Northern, Stirling's Single and, a couple of generations later, the large Atlantic. In my opinion these are two of the finest looking, and in their time, performing, locomotives ever built, the lineage is there to be seen. However 10000 needed a revolutionary team, not evolutionary.

CHAPTER 2

The File

This section is primarily based on the file in the National Railway Museum York archive, which gives a detailed history of events through the life of the water tube and compound Hush-Hush. It would be useful at this point to refer to the Cast in Order of Appearance and the Drawing List in the appendices. The words in square brackets in the commentary are entirely mine but all else is from the file, albeit edited where necessary, without interpretation. The file is essentially the North Road Works related documentation. See *Yeadon's Register of LNER Locomotives* for the records relating to the running departments.

Phase 1: Design and Build

Hundreds of year's worth of engineers work before Gresley, Gresley himself and the people he worked with and the associated events are all vital to the understanding of the Hush-Hush project. That which follows describes the design, construction and running of what I believe could have been the ultimate steam machine. It is both climax and anticlimax as the use of oil took a grip of the world.

The first document in the file is a blueprint. This must have shocked Gresley and prepared him well for what was to come, at least with 10000, if not in other areas of his life. There was no room for the crew in the cab! The date was 19th April 1926.

The first letters in the file are dated 16th July 1926. One accompanied drawings to The Chief Mechanical Engineer noting the changes made since the previous issues. The evaporative surface had been increased and the heating surface decreased, resulting in the same total heating surface as the original design. Adjustments had been made to the superheater to revert to the original area, having shortened the boiler. The combustion chamber had also been reduced. The other letter, on the same date, was a note from W.E. Dalby with some feedback on performance expected from the steam produced by the new 350psi boiler and superheater. Dalby does state here that the boiler would probably be less efficient on the railway than the locomotive boiler. The first letter mentioned above is very formal, sent to the position not the personality. Occasionally less formal names were used, usually letters asking for and giving advice or in memos. For example Professor Dalby referred to Gresley as "My Dear Gresley" but this kind of informality was an exception.

The file continues with "fine tuning" of the design whilst doing battle to keep the machine within the envelope and power of the A1 Pacific. The subsequent changes made to the boiler to reduce overall length only produced a longer machine, whatever was done.

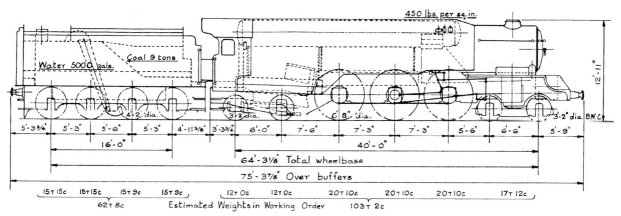

PROPOSED 4-6-4 HIGH PRESSURE ENGINE – OCTOBER 1928

Diagram, October 1928. The primary aim of the project was to produce a more efficient boiler. This is the diagram produced after the final changes, before production. It is simply an A1 with a water-tube boiler. The additional carrying wheels were necessitated by the length of the boiler. It was a compound to make good use of the additional pressure, but constrained to have the same power as the A1. (Ken Hoole Collection)

HUSH-HUSH – The Story of LNER 10000

On 30th July 1926, in a letter from W.E. Dalby to "Dear Gresley", the parameters were laid down for the Engines. A "three cylinder, high pressure, 2 stage, compound loco". One high-pressure and two low-pressure cylinders, 62.5% cut off in the high pressure cylinder with a corresponding 15 to 20% in each of the low, in normal working. The high-pressure cylinders took steam at 350psi and the low at the same as the A1, 180psi. The power output was to be the same as the A1 but with only two charges of steam per revolution instead of six! 20 years later, Chapelon was to prove with 2-4-2 A1 that this would have worked supremely, albeit producing far more horse power than Gresley was looking for.

By 18th August 1926, "The Superheater Company Limited" were involved. [It is of note that they, in the same period, designed the boiler for the ultra-high-pressure Royal Scot *Fury* for the LMS.]

A letter to A.C. Stamer on 27th September 1926 refers to schemes for carrying the back end. By now Gresley was well and truly resigned to a longer machine with the need for an extra pair of carrying wheels. The machine was to be a 4-6-4.

By Saturday 16th October 1926 we have evidence of some strange goings on. A meeting was scheduled with the LMS to discuss using the Midland Compound arrangement for the 4-4-0 Engines [D49] being built, including, "and bring along the high-pressure boiler engine drawings". I have no idea as to what was said at the meeting, or if the LMS saw the 10000 drawings, but it certainly seemed to throw a spanner in the works. One week after the meeting of Tuesday the 19th Gresley received a letter from W.E. Dalby: "My Dear Gresley, One or two important points have emerged from our discussion last week". Gresley was now talking of a normal cut off of 40% in the high-pressure cylinder and with three cylinders, only one high-pressure, this would not work due to lack of steam for exhaust in some operating conditions. The letter suggested that Gresley look at the "German Engine" to see what was going on there. He clearly did as it appears in the paper that he wrote in 1931, however this did not change things, Gresley did not revert to his original ideas and a rethink was necessary.

[On 17th October, Gresley celebrated his twenty-fifth wedding anniversary. The family photograph has Ethel Francis, wife of Gresley seated in front. She was not well and this showed on the expressions of the devoted family. Two years, to the day, after this photograph Ethel Francis was diagnosed with terminal cancer. Please stop for one moment and think of this and the inevitable stress that this must have caused.

Gresley would surely need a very strong team around him under these terrible circumstances.]

On 22nd October 1926, a letter to Mr S. Symes of the LMS from R.J. Robson of the LNER stated that the design of the cylinders for the compound engines, plural, had not yet begun.

On the 9th November, 10000 became a 4-6-4 W1 350psi four-cylinder "compound" with a letter outlining how this would work. Two fundamentally different methods of operation were being suggested, which offer an explanation to the phases in the life of the extra-high-pressure machine. The first proposal was to have 10.37in high-pressure cylinders in which the two would act as one providing together only 31% of the starting effort. The second option was 13.06in high-pressure cylinders to give an even starting effort over all four cylinders. Notice the first proposal would mimic a three cylinder machine but with cranks at 90 + 90 + ½@90 + ½@90 approximately 3@ 90 + 135 + 135.

By the 19th November 1926, we have a 4-6-4, four-cylinder compound, starting at 80% cut off and running at 50% cut off in the high-pressure cylinders with a long cut off in the low-pressure cylinders. Options were high-pressure cylinders of 12 or 12½in diameter, low-pressure 18 or 18½in, producing 1800 indicated horsepower at 50 miles per hour with the work evenly spread over four cylinders. Comparative data was produced for ex-North Eastern 4-4-2, PLM 4-6-2, PLM 4-8-2 and the proposed LNER 4-6-4 four-cylinder compound.

In the mean time, letters were being exchanged regarding the boiler and associated problem solving until 23rd December 1926, when the first move to a higher pressure was made. Reference was made to an assumption of 10⅜in diameter high-pressure cylinders and 18in low-pressure cylinders worked at 40% cut off high pressure and 70% low pressure. "However the CME wishes for 50% in the high pressure and the boiler pressure should be taken at 400lbs." The resulting cylinder sizes for various conditions were discussed and 10⅜in was still favoured. The letter continues "I have always understood that a late cut off in the L.P. kept constant whilst the H.P. cut off is decreased with increasing speed is the most efficient method." Likewise the receiver was to be kept to a minimum for most efficient working. [Both of these were to be proven wrong. In fact André Chapelon showed that quite the opposite was the case!]

Whilst it had been established that the machine needed additional carrying wheels at the back end, it was some time before serious consideration was given to how this would be achieved. The suggestion of a trailing box of the Pacific engine type augmented by another pair on a pony truck was documented on 27th June 1927. On the 4th August 1927 a meeting was held with Mr Gresley to consider various details. A suggestion was made that, due to having an additional trailing truck, it would be possible to make the grate bigger with a consequence of a more powerful machine. Clearly Gresley had not got the message across. He did not want a more powerful machine and continued to assert this throughout the project.

A letter from A.C. Stamer to Gresley on 5th August 1927 was accompanied by drawing 6167, "which Messrs Davies & Metcalfe have supplied of a special high pressure injector…into the boiler against a pressure of 450 lbs per square inch." The locomotive had become a 4-6-4 450psi four-cylinder compound.

A letter dated 22nd August 1927 requested "The sketch should shew if a rotary valve gear could be easily worked in and should only shew sufficient information for this purpose"

10th November 1927 produced a rather scathing letter from Gresley. He had seen a gradual increase in the grate area and, during a period away, a further significant increase had been made. Gresley instructed the team to get it back to 40 square feet to match the standard Pacific as the whole object was to reduce steam consumption: "We do not now require a more powerful engine".

[One commentator regarding the Hush-Hush story asserts that the few runs logged by enthusiasts were rated no better than a fair Gresley Pacific performance. Gresley got it spot on, however the tone of the reports suggests that more was expected by the uninformed casual observer, which added strength to the poor reputation that has stayed firmly glued to this machine.]

31st January 1928, memorandum, Meeting with Mr Marriner, includes, along with other boiler details, "Connection to be provided for H.P. steam to H.P. injector" [the significance of this will become clear later in this book].

A communication signed by Gresley on 1st

The boiler. *The long top steam drum and four bottom water drums are illustrated well in this photograph. Note the manhole doors for all the drums. The date is 16th January 1929. (Ken Hoole Collection)*

February 1928 stated: "With reference to the high pressure locomotive, the year's Building Programme to which this should be charged has not yet been decided, but I enclose Special Expenditure Order No 138 for collecting the wages and material charges."

By 27th February 1928, the frames had been ordered, however boiler details were still being thrashed out, practical clearances and access for (and minimising) maintenance being the main issues at this point. This machine had to be as easy to maintain as the standard Pacific. By now, A.L. Mellor at Yarrow felt compelled to state: "In fact the only correct thing that is left of any drawing previously made is the title". [He was lucky, even the title changed for the LNER men, several times!] Work was going on with the cylinders and the superheaters were in the final stages of design. Some difficulty was experienced with communication with The Superheater Company regarding the superheater design: "at the same time, he [Gresley] said he did not wish us to let them see all the drawings, neither were we to give them more information than was necessary for their requirements". [How much was necessary? It can't have been easy.]

At the end of April 1928: "H.P. cylinders 12in x 26in, cast steel, L.P. 20in x 26in, cast iron" were drawn up to give an even torque over four cylinders. The details of the interface between frame and boiler were being finalised and thoughts turned to uniting the boiler, at Yarrows, with the frames being built at Darlington. "I [R.J. Robson] find that the engine will negotiate a curve of 106 feet radius, with the coupled wheels and bissel truck left out altogether", this in reference to sending the frames to Yarrow to be united with the boiler there.

On 7th June 1928, a letter appears regarding the balancing of the new machine.

Drawings continued in significant number, fittings were well on in detail and suppliers' letters circulated in the second half of 1928. There was no problem in dealing with 450psi as this pressure was, by then, commonplace in steam engineering. In response to a letter from A.C. Stamer, Gresley decided to have the tender built at Doncaster, and an instruction to do this was given on the 30th July 1928, although Gresley said not to rush this through but to wait until the frames were ready to go to Messrs Yarrow.

[It has been suggested that the name Hush-Hush was coined at this point. The men at North Road, an eye witness says, told enquirers that the frames were for a "hush hush" job. However, Gresley was preparing for the International Railway Conference, Madrid, and he clearly had no intention of keeping the details of his locomotive a secret, but that was not to take place until 5th to 15th May 1930. Other people, ex-North Road, tell me that the machine was so quiet "it made a kind of hush hush sound, quite different to the other engines

The boiler firebox. Here we have a view of the new boiler from the firebox end. (Ken Hoole Collection)

and hence was named Hush-Hush". Both stories could quite well be true, some picking the name up at the works, others at the station. A visit to the British Pathé News Web site does not help because a newsreel prior to the introduction of 10000 refers to the NER dynamometer car as Hush-Hush and an almost identical caption introduces the W1 a few years later. Did British Pathé News coin the name? A bone of contention that can be cleared up here is a reference on 29th September 1928 regarding that front end. It was designed essentially to duct primary air to the fire grate, around the boiler casing and down the backhead to the ashpan rear. This was not "streamlining" as such, O.V.S. Bulleid was simply good at the synthesis of aesthetics, practicality and intuition creating a smooth, multifunctional, front end. Just like any work of art, some love it and others hate it.]

As previously mentioned, the boiler was to have had a connection for the high-pressure injector, yet 27th November 1928 produced a document from R.J. Robson to Davies & Metcalfe, that clearly did not get the attention it should. "There was confusion over the flanging of the injector and the steam was to be taken from the manifold". It is a pity that no one investigated the root cause of this mix up. On the 28th 1¾in injector feed pipes, plural, were mentioned by Davies & Metcalfe. At the same time discussions took place regarding the size of injector and the delivery pipe required now that the demand had reduced from the initial 28,000lb of water per hour to 20,000. No 10 initially, Gresley gave the instruction to proceed with No 9 on 3rd December 1928.

The boiler. *This is a rear, three-quarter view of the new boiler. Note the arrangement of the eight tubes that would straddle the fire hole door when fitted to the locomotive. (Ken Hoole Collection)*

Opposite page, top: Frames under construction at North Road. *The frames take shape at North Road on the Hush-Hush project. The boiler was suspended from the large bracket behind the cylinders and above the frames. (Ken Hoole Collection)*
Opposite page, bottom: Frames as shipped to Yarrow. *This is how the frames were shipped to Yarrow's Yard. There is no centre driver but all the other wheels are in place. Taken at North Road works. (Ken Hoole Collection)*
Above: Frames as Shipped to Yarrow. *Here we have a three quarter view of the frames ready for shipment to Yarrow. (Ken Hoole Collection)*

By 16th January 1929, the boiler was assembled and the frames took shape at Darlington North Road. North Road provided the material for the smokebox and footplating and Davies & Metcalfe were informed that the locomotive had steam brakes. Before March 20th 1929, the frames were at Yarrows, Glasgow. In a letter of this date there were instructions to have a new bogie centre casting made in preparation for replacement on the return of the locomotive to Darlington. Exchanges continued between the LNER and Yarrows, including modifications to the front end that included a completely new smokebox door, 3ft 1in, to replace the one first supplied. Details of the ashpan and cab windows were discussed.

By 30th July 1929, Mactaggart Scott & Co Ltd were involved with the final details of the telemotors for the reversing gear.

[17th October 1928 was Gresley's 27th wedding anniversary, which must have been the saddest occasion imaginable. His wife had been diagnosed with cancer and in the following ten months he carried on as best he could until, on the 5th August 1929, she died. In September, Gresley had to get away and he and his daughter Vi visited Canada. By November he was on the footplate of a booster fitted CPR 2-10-4 and was then ready to return to England.]

On 16th August 1929 the blastpipe was being readied and pipe runs determined. By 5th September the method of filling the boiler was an issue. The steam drum was to be drained from the smokebox end. Initially, blow down valves were to have been fitted to all four water drums and Gresley had subsequently suggested taper plugs but was advised against it, finally the decision was made to have hand holes secured by dogs.

On 10th September 1929, Mactaggart Scott were given the order for telemotor reverser and water cock operating gears, £225 net, delivered to Darlington.

Opposite page, top: *Original smokebox with template for change.* *As can be seen from this picture taken in the boiler shop at Yarrow's, the locomotive actually started in construction there with an A1 smokebox. This was rebuilt to accommodate the changes needed to get air to the rear of the firebox. The rebuilding process had begun in this view with the templates for what was to become that iconic front-end in place. (Ken Hoole Collection)*
Opposite page, bottom: *Side view in boiler shop at Yarrow's.* *From this view, again at Yarrow's, the distinctive slope is now formed. The front ducting has yet to be fitted. (Ken Hoole Collection)*
Above: *Smokebox with modified cladding commenced.* *In this view the second, smaller smokebox door can be seen. The air space between the boiler and cladding can be seen. (Ken Hoole Collection)*

The locomotive was transformed from the A1 front end to what was, for a short time, to become standard for new designs, mainly due to the visual impact in that Art Deco period. On 25th September 1929 "the tender with wedges, tools, lifting blocks, sheets etc is leaving here today". This was in preparation for the move from Yarrow to Darlington. The locomotive was lined up at Yarrow's yard for a photo shoot with dummy centre drivers and side rod. The trailing truck had to be removed to get the locomotive out of the yard, which is why a tender full of gear was needed to extricate the locomotive. I do not know how or why the cladding around the rear water drum on the right hand side became flattened, but the locomotive ran for some months before this was tidied up. The locomotive move involved travelling LMS lines and letters were exchanged regarding how this

was to be done. On the one hand, sufficient detail had to be given to the LMS to satisfy them that the machine was fit to run over their lines, including profile, weights and a maximum speed of 20mph, but on the other hand, it was to be sheeted up before the LMS inspected the engine.

On 15th October 1929 the regulator was in discussion. This included the first of several references to the model at Darlington. However the nature of the model (the scale, etc) was not mentioned.

By 4th November 1929 the "Eight-wheel corridor tender for Darlington" was ready for despatch. [When this was received, modifications were made to suit 10000 and a drawing still exists to show these. A close inspection of the tender, now behind 60009, confirms the modifications and the origin of this tender.]

Above, left: *Outside at Yarrow, cab view.* When Yarrows had completed their tasks, the locomotive was set up in the works yard for a photo shoot. The cab is ready for its fittings. *(Ken Hoole Collection)*

Above, right: *Outside at Yarrow, front view.* The ducts at the front end can be clearly seen in this view. *(Ken Hoole Collection)*

Below: *Outside at Yarrow, right hand view.* A dummy centre driver and side rod had been mocked up to give a better image. *(Ken Hoole Collection)*

The File

Left: *Outside at Yarrow, view from above.* The smoke lifting arrangements can be seen from this view. (Ken Hoole Collection)

Below: *Outside at Yarrow.* The cladding in the area of the rear water drum has suffered some damage. It was a while before this was tidied up. (Ken Hoole Collection)

[A method of treating the feed water, not as an absolute solution but to help, was with feedwater trays. These had been tried and tested several times in the past, as follows:

1863 G Spencer, GB, patented tray purifier in steam space. A number of trays one below the other.

1863 Herr Wagner, loco eng Bergish-Mmarkische Railway, Germany had similar.

1890 M Chapsal, France, again similar.

1906 Mr Vaughan suggested to Mr G.J. Churchward that he put top feed into the steam space and the GWR top feed resulted, including two parallel trays, inside the boiler, under the safety valve seating.

1917 Mr R.E.L. Maunsell, SE&CR, had a dome shaped chamber outside the boiler. Water flows down a helical tray inside this chamber, finally dropping on to a saddle fixed to the perforated steam pipe.

1929 Mr H.N. Gresley, LNER, tray purifier in steam drum of 4-6-4 extra high pressure locomotive.]

Gresley was signing the CME's letters by 5th November 1929, it having been H N GRESLEY pp during his absence. The *British Enterprise* nameplates were drafted at North Road on 20th November. They were drawn and cast but not fitted. The locomotive was returned, attached to tender 763 from a recently-withdrawn class S, 4-6-0, on 2nd December 1929, "PER LNER GOODS".

In the first week of December 1929 there was something of a drama regarding the injectors and cones. The demand was now calculated at 1500 gallons (15,000lb) of water per hour and replacement cones were needed urgently. At one point the high-pressure injector seemed to be lost in transit between Manchester and Darlington and people were panicking. A number of letters passed between the LNER and Gresham & Craven regarding this, setting the scene for something of a head-to-head between the two companies, which would not culminate for well over a year. A spare set of Dalglish firebars was ordered on 5th December 1929. The locomotive was ready to run on 12th December 1929, and did.

Outside the boiler shop. *It was felt that a man was required in the picture to give a sense of scale. (Ken Hoole Collection)*

Outside at Yarrow with mock up centre drivers and connection rod. *Ready to go to Darlington. "Sheet up for transport across LMSR metals" was the instruction. (Ken Hoole Collection)*

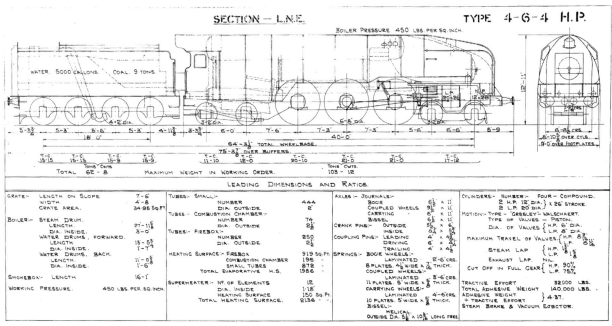

The diagram and details as built. (Ken Hoole Collection)

HUSH-HUSH – The Story of LNER 10000

The LMS ultra-high-pressure Royal Scot No 6399 *Fury* was introduced at the same time. This machine had an ultra-high-pressure primary circuit containing distilled water in a closed circuit. The firebox heat was applied to this, and because of the use of pure water, scale deposition was not an issue. The "working" steam was produced by heat exchange in a steam generator into which the primary circuit "coils" were immersed. This description will be recognised by the designers of today's nuclear systems. In fact *Fury* only needed a nuclear pile in the firebox and it could have run for months, only needing to stop for water and oiling around.

Ready to run on 12th December 1929. There was no front handrail at this point, and it would be quite a while before the locomotive was fit for purpose. (Ken Hoole Collection)

As built, with no front handrail no electric headlamps. This three-quarter view shows 10000 as originally built and as it ran on the first trial run. (Ken Hoole Collection)

32

This front view shows 10000 as originally built and as it ran on the first trial run. (Ken Hoole Collection)

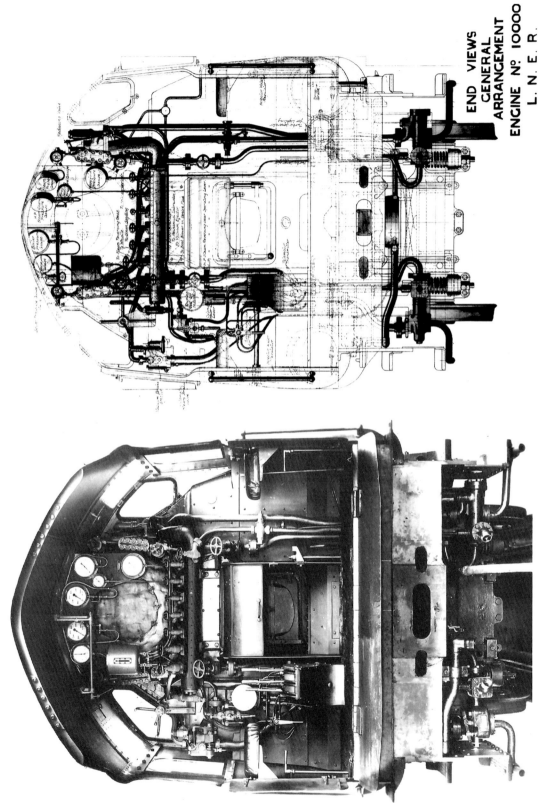

The Cab. Left: all cab fittings are in place and ready to go. Right: the general arrangement of the cab shows what the fittings were. (Both Ken Hoole Collection)

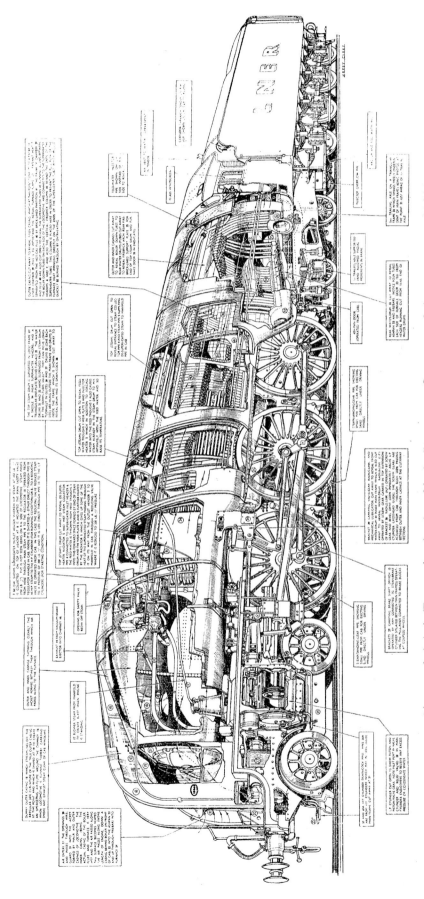

Chart of 4-6-4 Type 4-cylinder High Pressure Compound Locomotive 10000

Insides exposed for all to see. (Ken Hoole Collection)

The manifold. This was a tidy arrangement, but it did not work. Critically, it took some time to establish this. (Ken Hoole Collection)

Phase 2: Running In to Fit For Purpose

On 12th December 1929, 10000 made its first trial run with Charles Eltringham (Fireman) his dad, John (Driver) and two fitters.

After the first run, some details were tied up. There is a reference to 20,000lb of steam evaporated per hour, dated 18th December. [Surely the cones had been changed to deliver 15,000lb? Maybe this is part of the high-pressure injector saga, an early problem that was to delay progress for many tedious and frustrating months, and had nothing to do with the boiler or the engines, high pressure or low.] The first of many letters between the LNER and the producers of the auxiliary equipment, including the high-pressure injector were written at this time, all to do with unsatisfactory auxiliary fittings.

Driver Fireman and Fitters. Left to right – Charles Eltringham (Fireman) his Dad, John (Driver) and two fitters on the day of the first trial trip, 12th December1929. (Ken Hoole Collection)

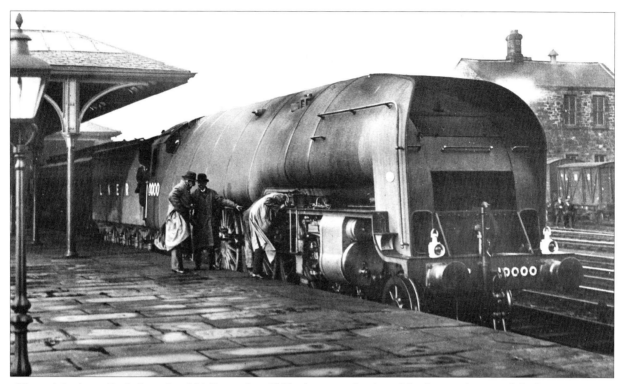

First trial trip to Croft Junction 12th December 1929. Again on the day of the first trial trip and the locomotive gets a close inspection by Gresley. The alternative source of the name Hush-Hush might be caught here. The two men in the right background have heard this machine for the first time, and it makes a kind of hush hush sound, not the bark of a conventional locomotive. (Ken Hoole Collection)

Darlington. The trial run to Croft Junction and back. Note that the front handrail was not fitted at this time. (Ken Hoole Collection)

Line up of Fitters. *This image shows the fitters involved in the construction of 10000. Sixth and eleventh from the left are the two who accompanied 10000 on the first trip of the 12th December 1929. The man in the bowler hat on the extreme right is Thomas Heppie Simpson who is remembered by his daughter, Marjorie, as Works Foreman. This picture was probably taken just before or after the locomotive was moved to Stooperdale from its home shed in the locomotive works yard, for official photographs. It was certainly after the first main line trip because it originally ran with no front handrail but this was fitted within days, and definitely by the 29th December 1929. (Roger Brian's Collection)*

Above: Line up of Locomen. *Thomas Heppie Simpson with drivers, firemen and cleaners. One can only imagine that these are the men allocated to drive locomotives in or around the works. The crews for the main line were a select band, requested by name and individually instructed to attend the works from elsewhere. The track suggests that this is in front of the shed, especially built for 10000, in the locomotive works yard, probably very late 1929 or early 1930. (Roger Brian's Collection)*

Right: Rail level view, Darlington. *Note that the lamps were simple oil-filled ones, avoiding the complication of electricity at this point. (Ken Hoole Collection)*

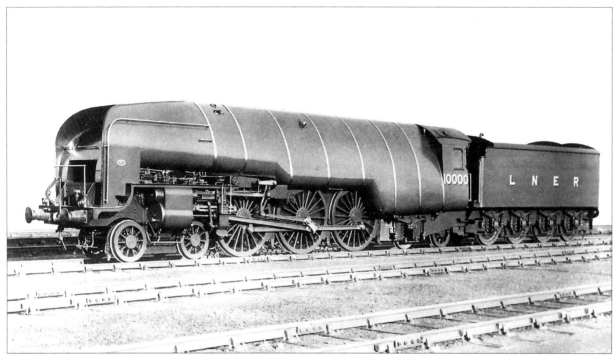

Darlington photograph taken on the driver's side. *The locomotive was only days old and the handrail was in place. (Ken Hoole Collection)*

10000 passing Springfield Junction. *Taken on 29th December 1929, this time on a trip to York and back. (Ken Hoole Collection)*

At York. *Looking immaculate. (Ken Hoole Collection)*

On the York trip. *A well-known picture of 10000. (Ken Hoole Collection)*

Above, left: Firebox with the cladding removed. With the inspection cover off, clearly there is little build up and it can be seen that anything that tries to accumulate soon flakes off.
Above, right: Pre-heat section with cladding removed. With more inspection covers off, this pre-heat section of the boiler is pretty clean. Some water tubes have no build up at all. You can get a feel for the air space between the boiler casing and the outer cladding from this view. (Both, Ken Hoole Collection)

The locomotive was further tested on 29th December 1929, operating from its home shed, specially built, in Darlington North Road Locomotive Works yard. The shed had a coaling dock with specially prepared and weighed stocks of coal. It is highly likely that the tender at the front of the queue on the left hand side of the loading dock in the early days of the locomotive was the one prepared for and initially paired with 10000, ex-class S 4-6-0, the S class being withdrawn at about this time with only one exception. That was the counter pressure engine that survived to be sent to the new testing station at Rugby, when it finally came to fruition.

By 29th December 1929, the front handrail was fitted. On 30th December, after a York trial, larger cones were requested for the Davies & Metcalfe injector because the existing ones were considered inadequate. The Gresham & Craven high-pressure injector was not a reliable starter and required adjusting, it was thought, and Gresham & Craven were informed of this on the same day. By 31st December, Mr P.R. Gresham had visited North Road and found that the only fault was slightly damaged cones, not their doing, but replacements were prepared as a courtesy. The locomotive was not in steam during his visit. The next steaming was to be 6th January 1930. Of major significance, Mr J.N. Gresham was confined to bed

during this early period and could only send a representative.

On 1st January 1930, Siemens offered to supply electrical equipment for indicating valve positions. Letters continued between the LNER and injector suppliers.

On 2nd January 1930, the boiler was given a detailed inspection. In the whole file there is not one reference to leaky tubes as being a problem and the same applies here. Gresley's later paper states quite categorically that there were none. [It could be that leaks did occur, and the method of repair, being non-standard, could have been perceived as problematic on the shop floor, but the standard Stephenson boiler is forever in need of attention regarding tubes and they are taken up as a matter of routine along with the leaky stays and seams. Leaks in one type of boiler must be taken in context of how they compare with another.] The report describes the deposition of scale, the state of the tubes, and ash; little is said of how the boiler compared with others having had the same working hours. However I have extracted the comments that have some value in the context of this book.

"The whole boiler was considered to be in very good condition … desirable to brush the tubes … to set up a standard of cleanliness … there was no distortion of the tubes … the bars were not burned … the brickwork was in first class condition … The brick column at the entrance to the centre of the flue was loose at the top but will not fall down ... Mr Stamer remarked that the dust was much smaller than is found in the Pacific type locomotives (it is generally about ⅛in across) … it is suggested that a vacuum cleaner would be very useful for cleaning between the tubes".

On 8th January 1930, Stones wrote to the LNER in reference to the four standard headlamps, sent for the purpose of electrifying, and stated that four of the glasses were broken, presumably in transit. More important than this was the first visit to Kings Cross of 10000. As you will see, the machine was far from ready for such a public appearance and Gresley must have been under a great deal of pressure to make the run. [I can't help thinking of the APT in more recent times, albeit electric; the similarities in the story are startling. The APT was functioning perfectly in its last year when my family and I had the privilege of riding on it. Only the footplate of an LNER Pacific at full speed can beat it for a thrill.] On 8th January, 10000 paid its first visit to Kings Cross. As well as the stills, there exists a short movie of the locomotive [go to the British Pathé News

Website to see this], going to be turned, with the paparazzi of the day scurrying alongside with their huge cameras getting those precious shots for media release, just as if it were a film star. Several of the Kings Cross stills were, no doubt, taken by them. One of the stills (see page 45) shows the cameraman taking the movie from the edge of the turntable pit. By 13th January, the photographs were being circulated by the LNER to those who mattered.

On 15th January 1930, an examination of the air ducts and smokebox, carried out by T. Ferguson and Shop Boiler Inspector Lowther, was reported on. Reference was again made to small ashes along with dust and soot. The worst was "a heap of ashes 1" deep". Yes, one inch! Conventional boilers often had that much AFTER they had been cleaned. Also on this date, the electric indicator idea was dropped.

On 16th January 1930, R.J. Robson asked Yarrow when he could expect the drawing showing "the position of thermometer at drum end, the best position for the smokebox and the expected temperature in the firebox; we wish to order the pyrometer". On 18th January 1930, drawing 13875.D was issued, detailing the new blastpipe and tops and associated cone.

10000's first visit to the capital. *This view was almost certainly taken at Kings Cross on 8th January 1930. (Ken Hoole Collection)*

This page, top left: Kings Cross on the 8th January 1930. Daughters Violet and Marjorie stand with Gresley whilst the Eltringhams, father and son, watch from the cab. Gresley must have so wished that his wife could have been there but cancer took her away the previous year.

This page, top right: Gresley at the regulator with his daughters behind him. He is unaware of the months of problems ahead. One can still stand on the tender footplate today but in the company of 60009.

Left: Front view taken at Stooperdale for publicity purposes. The blow off drain pipe carried in the first weeks, up to and including the first visit to Kings Cross, which would be behind the middle lamp, has now been removed.

Opposite page, top: Kings Cross, 8th January 1930. The locomotive is not yet fit for purpose but, like the APT of more recent times, politics forced the run.

Opposite page, bottom: 10000 being turned on the first visit of the machine to Kings Cross. The cameraman in the foreground of this picture is making a movie.
(All Ken Hoole Collection)

Broadside view, again the first trip to the capital. *The firebox cladding still needs attention. (Ken Hoole Collection)*

On 27th January 1930, Driver Eltringham and his mate were requested to be at Darlington Works by 9am on Thursday, 30th instant, for an 11am departure from Darlington. On the 29th, this trip to York was rescheduled to leave Haughton Bridge sidings at 10.55am. On this day, the oiling of the axleboxes became a more pressing issue as "complaint was made that the driver could not see whether the oil was going into the filler or not". The next scheduled trip was 350 to 400 tons from Darlington to Doncaster on Thursday 6th February 1930, "leaving Darlington shortly after 9am … Driver Eltringham and his mate to stay overnight and sign in at the Works at 7am." "A corridor coach next to the engine … it would be as well if your Foreman and fitters travelled with the special as usual".

29th January 1930, the following was produced:

Balls for Testing Tubes for Scale

Outside Dia	Inside Dia	Ball Dia	Length of Chain
2"	1.68	1.62	5' 6"
2½"	2.012	1.95	7' 0"
2½"	2.192	2.06	7' 0"

6 Balls for each Size

On 3rd February 1930, drawings were issued detailing new pattern high-pressure piston valve back cylinder covers and liners. A new arm was to be made on the high-pressure way shaft and alteration to the crosshead on the high-pressure steam reversing gear cylinder. "The new piston valve liners will necessitate boring the HP cylinders, further in, to accommodate the new liners. … This will complete the modification to the valve gear … when the engine comes in" [after the run on 6th February]. A further run was scheduled for Thursday 13th February, 500 tons, Darlington to Kings Cross, returning the next day. The Chief Locomotive Draughtsman was to accompany the special.

On the 11th February 1930, Gresley asked A.C. Stamer for photographs of the locomotive, "from both sides, from both ends and from above" in order that a paperweight model could be made. "Special care must be taken not to move the engine so the rods may be in their correct relative position on both sides."

On 14th February 1930: "Larger H.P. injector cones please." [Still treating the symptoms.]

19th February, "Electric lights ordered £77. 5. 0. Including all fixtures and fittings."

21st February, "New cam required for cut off indicator."

23rd February, to Perth.

Taken from above, at Kings Cross. *By the 13th of January these pictures were circulated to everyone that needed to see them. (Ken Hoole Collection)*

Tender first in a station. *Mundane carriage stock movements were clearly carried out. (Ken Hoole Collection)*

At Kings Cross. *By the time this picture was taken the firebox cladding has been sorted out. (Ken Hoole Collection)*

The File

The Perth Test, 23rd February 1930

"The trial was made over this route with a train weighing 406 tons including the dynamometer car in order to test the performance of the engine on heavy gradients". [Knowing what I do about the locomotive, in retrospect, it was quite futile, although at the time was considered significant. The report is full of excuses, including blaming a photographer for delays on the Forth Bridge. I do know that the locomotive had to ease back at frequent intervals in these early months due to an almost unbelievable oversight in the construction, and consequently, the value of this data is limited.] Here are a few significant extracts, to satisfy the story.

The report states: "Difficulties were experienced with the high pressure injector and a good deal of water was wasted due to this." [This would also result in easing of the locomotive as the boiler pressure would have been depleting rapidly, especially up steep hills, and this, of course, results in loss of time.] The report, at one point, states "with a steady boiler pressure of 430 lbs per square inch". The timing and record sheet tells a different story with the boiler reaching 430psi only once, at 11 55AM and for no more than a few minutes.

Some of the data from this run is reproduced here:

Start Edinburgh	1102	Boiler Pressure	400psi
			400psi
			430psi
			420psi
Perth	1240		290psi
		Average	353psi

Other than the peak at 1155 [1149 Dunfermline, 1156 Town Hill Junction] the Boiler Pressure varied from 275 to 400psi.

Start Perth	1452	Boiler Pressure	420psi
Dalmeny	1620		320psi
		Average	376psi

Boiler pressure varied from 320 to 420psi

At Reston Junction on the way to Edinburgh for Perth. *Hush-Hush heads for Perth for hill-climbing tests with dynamometer car in tow, still not fit for purpose, but no one seemed to know why. (Ken Hoole Collection)*

HUSH-HUSH – The Story of LNER 10000

[By this time it had already become clear that the locomotive worked fine when it was standing still but as soon as it moved, auxiliary equipment began to fail. The tests at Yarrows were fine (see the *Gresley Observer* No 141 Autumn 2006 pages 50/1 for evidence of this) to the point where it was considered acceptable to reduce the demand for water by 25%, although even at Yarrows there was some injector trouble. It is clear to me that this was the start of the water-tube boiler's reputation of being unsuitable for a rolling chassis and it is easy to understand why, given the early test results and the locomotive's behaviour. Imagine being on the footplate of a locomotive, at full throw, consuming up to 2000 gallons per hour. The injectors have to match this or, if you don't slow down, the boiler will fail. The injectors work for a while and then go off intermittently. The fitter looks at the fireman, bewildered. "This is not normal, they usually work or they don't. Better ease off". It seemed to be that the injectors would not work with the boiler moving.]

By 26th February 1930, 10000 had entered the works to have the valve gear altered, as we have already detailed, and the problem with oiling of the axleboxes was dealt with.

A letter from C.W.L. Glaze to A.C. Stamer on the 1st March 1930 gave details of relative positions of the radial indicator markings and valve rod positions, both on the drawings and the locomotive. He indicated that there was variance and asked which was correct. New elements "which are to be put in" were mentioned on 4th March and on the same date an instruction for alterations to the blastpipe and chimney. A reply to the letter from Glaze on 6th March suggests that the variance might be due to the existing cam and that a new one is to be fitted. The letter makes it clear that the problem was one of accuracy rather than error. "The difference between the two readings is such, that we can take either." On the same date, more new cones.

Gresley, referring to discussions with Mr Yarrow regarding the constructions [plural] of the model of Engine No 10000, 1in to the foot [as is the one at North

Hush-Hush on the Perth test, passing Dunfermline (Lower) on 23rd February 1930. Gresley must have been frustrated at having to go through this time consuming, complicated and inconclusive way of testing. As it happened, the locomotive was not fit for purpose at this time and the results were meaningless. (The Ken Hoole Collection)

Crossing the Forth Bridge. *The photographer got the blame for the delays which in reality were caused by intermittently failing auxiliaries. (Ken Hoole Collection)*

Road that fired me up in the first place] wrote to Messrs Yarrow & Co Ltd "to know if you are arranging to put the work in hand". On 10th March, Gresley wrote to Stamer, "I will arrange for the necessary photographs to enable to Van Cytenbeek Sales Company to prepare the paperweights."

11th March 1930, and I find a letter from Gresham & Craven Ltd, concerning more injector woes. On 14th March the electric headlamps were delivered but, more importantly, a report from Gresham & Craven Ltd was issued indicating that the bench tests of the injector showed it to be in perfect working order and suggesting that the LNER send one of their own engineers to see for themselves. Gresley replied by the 17th March that, "injectors are always apt to be rather fickle and this one appears to be more so than usual", the suggestion was that it is on the locomotive that it must work perfectly and that he [J.N. Gresham] should see for himself, on the footplate, when the locomotive is next in steam. J.N. Gresham accepted the invitation.

On the 24th March 1930, a Saturday meeting between Mr Hogg (Yarrows), Mr Drynan (Cockburns)

and R.J. Robson (LNER) was detailed indicating the changes to be made to the safety valves, 2½in to 1½in.

I have read reports of 10000 having a very difficult regulator, and evidence of this appears in a letter of 31st March reading, "Since the regulator has been re-assembled on the engine, we find the pull rod from the reversing screw in cab will not meet the lever on the regulator valve, and we cannot understand how this has got out of position." The reply to this on the 3rd April suggested that the spindle head portion is now slightly higher, causing the problem, and that it is not a bad thing as this will help as the valve wears and in the process will return to the original position. It was, however, suggested that an adjustment piece be added.

Drawings were forwarded to Gresley regarding the paperweight model, and on 7th April 1930 he told Stamer that "this will not do" as there was too much detail. By 8th April, Edward Thompson was writing letters and on this occasion referred to the variance between the engine and the drawing with respect to the low-pressure indicator rod and that the drawing should not be "worked to".

Above: At Edinburgh. *The signalmen must be amazed. (Ken Hoole Collection)*

Opposite page, top: *Is it a front handrail or somewhere to hang test gear? Here on test at Croft Spa, just south of Darlington, the 6ᵗʰ May 1930. (Ken Hoole Collection)*

Opposite page, bottom: At Croft Spa. *Another view taken of the test on the 6ᵗʰ May 1930. (Ken Hoole Collection)*

A steaming was planned for 15ᵗʰ April 1930, and Gresham & Craven were asked "for your representative to be present". Drawings of the revised components and arrangements were exchanged during April, but in particular Gresley requested coloured copies of the general arrangement drawings 14017D and 14018D for presentation to the Science Museum of South Kensington.

Trial runs are noted for Monday 5ᵗʰ May 1930. [These might not have happened, or the locomotive failed.] Note that the driver and fireman had been changed. On 5ᵗʰ May a proposed exhibition was postponed. On 13ᵗʰ May the exhibition was rescheduled to Saturday/Sunday 24/25ᵗʰ May, to take place at Cambridge; the locomotive moving on the 23ʳᵈ.

10000 was intended to be an experimental engine. To give a flavour of the attitude of the running staff to this locomotive, and their failure to understand what it was all about, I quote a letter of 27ᵗʰ June 1930 from the Locomotive Running Superintendent to the Assistant Chief Mechanical Engineer:

"Apparently it is intended that the really big manhole door cover should be taken off and the mudhole door withdrawn from the inside, but this is a very lengthy operation and really a waste of time when only ordinary boiler washing is to be carried out. The mudhole doors should be made standard"

[Clearly he was not aware that washing out had been given consideration in the design development stage and the best solution found. In this case it is not the business of the running department to be so presumptuous as to suggest that the standards of the day would prevail in the future and maybe what they were looking at would become the norm. Only experience would solve the maintenance problems. Incidentally, I don't see, "however we have saved considerable time not having to caulk up the stays and seams, as we do with the standard design boiler".

North Road works yard on 6th May 1930. *This view confounds the record with respect to "in works for attention". This is 10000's home shed, not "in works". The first tender attached to 10000 is at the end of the coaling stage to the left of the W1. We see carefully measured and tested coals alongside. The shed survived as a paint store until the works closed in 1966. The lines were removed but it is possible that one wall of the shed remains in the petrol station yard. (Ken Hoole Collection)*

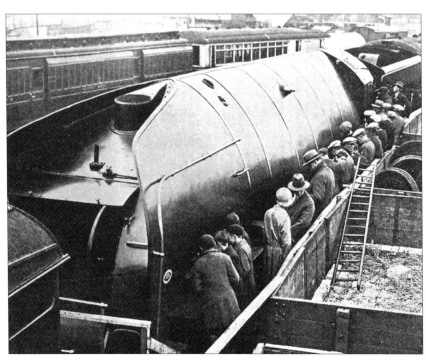

10000 was used as an exhibit for several charity exhibitions. *This one is at Cambridge on 24th May 1930. Notice the other water-tube boilered machine in the background, the Sentinel railcar. (Ken Hoole Collection)*

This view is again at Cambridge on 24th May 1930. (Ken Hoole Collection)

A striking rear view of the W1 at Cambridge on 24th May 1930. The vertical flat sides of the corridor tender do not do justice to the curved lines of 10000. There were modifications in the area of the front handrails but curved sides would have blended locomotive, tender and coaching stock very nicely. Maybe that was intended at a later date. (Ken Hoole Collection)

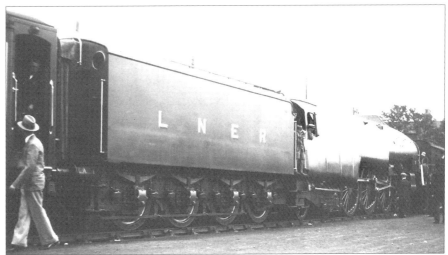

The train spotters have a field day. I wonder if those kids are still alive, about ninety years old by now, in 2010. Cambridge 24th May 1930. (Ken Hoole Collection)

People sometimes fail to realise that, to make overall maintenance easier, one or two tasks might become harder.]

A burden that was imposed on 10000 was the testing of fog apparatus. As an experimental machine this makes perfect sense; however, given that the locomotive was yet to prove itself fit for purpose, to add further experimental equipment unrelated to the job in hand was not helpful. On 2nd July 1930, a letter and sketch showed this, in as much as that the apparatus failed, in fact, according to the sketch, the handle fell off. Combine this with the still intermittently failing auxiliaries and the fireman's nightmare is complete. However, the file notes that: "the Pullman still arrived at Leeds on time". On the same day Yarrows politely reminded Gresley that it was agreed that "the drum end should be taken off when making the joint on the small door" I notice that the letters following this, to Darlington, state that it was their [Yarrows] intention that the drum end be taken off [suggesting not

Gresley's]. The record shows this to be a joint agreement based on structural integrity. [Personally, I fail to see the problem with removing the door on the drum end to see what is going on. In my experience, blind washing out results in gallons of water and time being wasted, poking about to see if the water space is clean, in an unseen space. Many a clogged throat and resultant damage comes from leaving behind mud bridges, not seen by the cleaner.] However, by 16th July, a drawing was prepared with a modification to allow the small mud doors to be removed independent to the end doors.

On 18th July 1930, Mr J.H. Smeddle wrote to the Assistant CME regarding: "11.32 Passenger, York to Newcastle, 11.7.30 Engine No 10000. – The fog apparatus causes a delay of 4 Mins. … perhaps you will write me saying what alterations you propose to make."

More auxiliary grief followed as, on 20th July 1930, the reducing valve was thoroughly cleaned but with no improvement, "can Mr Drynan [Cockburns]

A regular turn for the W1 was the Pullman via Ripon and Leeds. The handle fell off on the experimental fog apparatus during one of these runs. This is 21st June 1930. (Ken Hoole Collection)

Passing Darlington on 26ᵗʰ June 1930. (Ken Hoole Collection)

On the Pullman again. This time departing Newcastle. (Ken Hoole Collection)

Above: 10000 was entrusted with the Flying Scotsman, in spite of troubles with auxiliaries. However it still ran to schedule and is seen arriving at Kings Cross on 31ˢᵗ July 1930. (Ken Hoole Collection)

Opposite page, top: On the platform at Kings Cross. Gresley stands next to the two crews responsible for the locomotive on this run, 31ˢᵗ July 1930. (Ken Hoole Collection)

Opposite page, bottom: The driver and fireman of Hush-Hush become famous. Pictures of them were inset on this post card. (Ken Hoole Collection)

examine the valve on Monday the 28ᵗʰ when the engine will be laid off". [Notice that all of the auxiliary problems have been dealt with by treating the symptoms, up to this time, but is there a more fundamental flaw?]

On 23ʳᵈ July 1930, Mr P.R. Gresham saw the injector in steam both at Newcastle and during the trip from there to York, "whilst the engine was standing it [the injector] worked perfectly". The theory on this occasion was that the injector was not getting enough water and something must be choked. "We understand that the engine is to be at Darlington on Monday for cleaning". It was requested that this be checked. Darlington works was 10000's home shed, for cleaning, not "in works for attention". On 31ˢᵗ July, "Coal

Slacker – Engine No 10,000. ...as to when they can be fitted". More auxiliary steam required. By 1ˢᵗ August, the inevitable [in retrospect] report that there was no blockage, with respect to the injector, was produced.

Several letters went to and from Cockburns in this period, still concentrating on a perceived problem with the reducing valve including, on 6ᵗʰ August 1930, "this is very urgent as this engine is laid up". A report dated 14ᵗʰ August gave strong clues as to the problems with the auxiliaries: "The high pressure injector was then operated and our representative found that when the steam valve for this was opened quickly the reducing valve was rendered inoperative, the outlet pressure rising until the relief valve was blowing off. Immediately the injector valve was closed again the

58

reducing valve was quite satisfactory. … [Under running conditions] a tendency for the reducing valve to chatter". In the same report, damage to the diaphragm was reported, resulting from failure to adjust after grinding in. The LNER clearly ground this in on a regular basis, assuming that the chatter was due to steam "passing by", resulting in considerable loss of valve seat, which would need compensation. [No conclusions were stated but I suspect that Cockburns might have deduced the problem. How do you tell your customer, on whom your future depends, that they have made a schoolboy error that has dogged a prestigious and important project for almost a year?] Cockburns agreed to overhaul the damaged reducing valve. The valve was despatched by passenger train to speed up the process.

On 20th August 1930, Bassett-Lowke Ltd contacted Gresley regarding a request from the American Museum of Science and Industry for a 1in to 1ft model of the "English locomotive which is equipped with a Yarrow type of boiler". Would he be prepared to supply sufficient detail for a model?

By 21st August 1930, the reducing valve had been overhauled and bench tested and, of course was quite satisfactory. Cockburns do mention "modified the main valve portion to obviate the chatter" but whether they did will remain a mystery as there was nothing wrong with the design of the valve in the first place. On the same day, the LNER was writing to Cockburns about the regulator valve blowing and can Mr Drynan come and examine the regulator. [I believe that patience on all sides was starting to wear a little thin.] The LNER would send him a ticket for the journey.

On 28th August 1930, some trouble with the superheater tubes was noted, "sketch no 13955D of the worst group". Mr Clear of the Superheater Company took away a sample of the tube. On the same day, Gresley requested drawings for Bassett-Lowke Ltd. R.J. Robson wrote to Yarrow & Co on 28th August regarding the replacement of the mud hole doors with blow-off cocks, and the valves were ordered by the 29th August.

At Reston on 12th July 1930. *(Ken Hoole Collection)*

L.N.E.R. HIGH-PRESSURE COMPOUND EXPRESS LOCOMOTIVE No. 10,000
LEAVING WAVERLEY STATION, EDINBURGH
DESIGNED BY MR H. N. GRESLEY, C.B.E., CHIEF MECHANICAL ENGINEER OF THE L.N.E.R. AND BUILT AT THEIR WORKS IN DARLINGTON.

CYLINDERS (2), H.P.	12 INS. 26 INS.	BOILER	YARROW GRESLEY WATER TUBE
L.P.	20 INS. 26 INS.	PRESSURE	450 LBS PER SQ. IN.
DRIVING WHEELS DIAMETER	6 FT. 8 INS.	WEIGHT OF ENGINE & TENDER	166 TONS
LENGTH OVER BUFFERS	75 FT. 3 7/8 INS.		

Leaving Edinburgh. *On the up Flying Scotsman on 31st July 1930. (Ken Hoole Collection)*

L.N.E.R. "FLYING SCOTSMAN" TRAIN HAULED BY THE HIGH-POWER
LOCOMOTIVE No. 10,000

Passing Greenwood. *On the down Flying Scotsman on 1st August 1930. (Ken Hoole Collection)*

Above: Passing through York. *On the down Flying Scotsman on 1ˢᵗ August 1930. (Ken Hoole Collection)*

Opposite page, top: At Wavertree. *The W1 on exhibition again, this time it is the Liverpool and Manchester Centenary celebrations of 13ᵗʰ to 20ᵗʰ September 1930. (Ken Hoole Collection)*

Opposite page, bottom: A driver's side view at Wavertree. *September 1930. (Ken Hoole Collection)*

On 29ᵗʰ August 1930 it was noted that, "engine in steam on Wednesday next the 3ʳᵈ Proximal … Mr Drynan to report". The new fire door, drawing 14110.D. had been fitted by 6ᵗʰ September.

A report from Cockburns Ltd on 11ᵗʰ September 1930 shows that they were looking for anything that could explain the failure of their valve. [Their suggesting that there **might** have been a problem with the valve, rather than just insisting that it was fine, did not help to solve the problem with the auxiliaries. I feel sure that not everyone could believe that the problem with the auxiliaries was due to them all being faulty or temperamental. Some superficial commentators were almost certainly by this time giving the glib statement that "it is the inability of the water tube boiler to work on a rolling locomotive chassis". Someone must have worked it by now, surely?] Cockburns gave a good description of what was happening on the footplate and all of the clues are there, but they ended their report: "From the results of the trial run, we feel sure that these

fittings are quite satisfactory and can be relied on to perform their duties, if given a reasonable amount of attention, and maintained in good order".

The locomotive was not yet fit for purpose but Gresley had to move on. From an earlier document Gresley stated that there were two options for working the locomotive. One was to give an even torque over all four cylinders, which 12in cylinders approached; the other was to mimic a three-cylinder machine by letting each of the inside cylinders give half of the torque of the individual outside cylinders. 10in inside cylinders did just that. The locomotive was to be at the L&M Centenary Exhibition, Wavertree and on return to Darlington the high-pressure cylinders were to be lined up to 10in. Gresley instructed Reavell & Co to produce the liners on the 15ᵗʰ September 1930.

On 15ᵗʰ September 1930, the fourth locomotive in the Wavertree exhibition line up was No 10000. A later document suggests that 10000 was also exhibited at Manchester for these celebrations.

The File

Opposite page, top: What is it that draws people's attention to behind the rear driving wheel? Wavertree 15th September 1930. (Ken Hoole Collection)

Opposite page, bottom: W1 at Wavertree being prepared for shunting. The locomotive went on to Manchester to continue the L&M celebrations. (Ken Hoole Collection)

Right: Front view with electric lamps. Although this is not the best quality picture, it does show the arrangement of conduit on the front buffer beam and the electric lamps for which it was fitted. There was an issue with the electric lamps which must have caused some embarrassment. The works sent old lamps with broken glasses. I expect the contract called for refurbishment and therefore they thought that anything would do, but unfortunately not so. (Ken Hoole Collection)

Below: 10000 departs West Hartlepool. The steam sanders are on by the look of the train, which is on the way to Leeds on or around 7th July 1930. (Ken Hoole Collection)

Phase 3: Pseudo Three Cylinder

On 15th September 1930, the drawings for Bassett-Lowke Ltd were forwarded to Gresley. On 23rd September, Gresley instructed Stamer to hold the coloured drawings for the Science Museum.

On 24th September 1930, Gresley writes to Stamer informing him that he only intended Bassett-Lowke to have just sufficient external detail to make a representative model but he [Stamer] had forwarded every drawing produced to date and Gresley's letter includes "naturally I am not sending the whole of these".

During September and October 1930 a number of letters were exchanged regarding further changes to the superheater. However this was more of a reversion to the original arrangement as it is clear that Gresley felt that the original overheating problem was due to poor steam circulation in the superheater, rather than the proximity of the ends relative to the firebox, and Gresley had a solution to this in the use of appropriate baffling. Yarrows wanted to increase the superheat but Gresley had, yet again, to hold his team back in order to obtain a fair comparison with the standard Pacific; the superheaters must be as the standard Pacific.

13th October 1930, and P.A. Hyde contacted Mr Bulleid with respect to the Marcotty firebox door, which had a double purpose: to control the fire in the event of a blowback, and to help with cleaning the grate.

27th October 1930, and Cockburns were corresponding with Yarrows with respect to their fittings, but could only repeat their discussions with the LNER, other than to suggest a spring assist for the regulator valve, an idea that was taken up on the 3rd November.

During November 1930, the drawings of the superheater arrangements were circulating, along with the new 10in piston liners. [In passing, you might wonder how a 10in liner could be put into a 12in block without destroying the casting. The liner was in fact ribbed in order that it would flex and the cavities were then filled with white metal.]

10th November 1930, and correspondence was exchanged regarding the provision of a connection for a slaker pipe. More demand on the auxiliary steam supply.

On 18th December 1930, Gresley requests that the Science Museum drawings be finished. On this date, there is also reference to "Engine No 10000. Balanced Firehole Door & Details"; this sounds very much like part of the "Marcotty" scheme.

By 30th December, Yarrow & Co were finishing off the model.

31st December 1930, one year and a couple of weeks after the first trial, and the locomotive was still not fit for purpose. J.H. Gresham wrote to H.N.Gresley, Esq., saying he was confined to bed, but "Mr Percy Gresham went to Darlington yesterday". The engine was not under steam "but it would appear that the mouth of the combining cone had been a little damaged by a spanner" [I suggest that it was more a result of the Geordie fitter exclaiming "this f….n injecta" and the resultant hurling across the workshop floor that the cone will have suffered.]

On the 1st January 1931 Gresley was preparing his "PAPER ON "HIGH PRESSURE LOCOMOTIVES", and he requested the appropriate photographs. On 6th January the coloured prints for the Science Museum were forwarded with the note "these drawings do not embody all the latest modifications".

13th January 1931, and "a soda box for hanging in the water tank in which a linen bag containing soda can be placed" had been made to condition the feed water.

On 15th January 1931, photographs were again requested for the production of the proposed paperweight model. Mr Harper telephoned for two pictures of 10000 to be sent to Institution of Mechanical Engineers, London, for "the exhibition on Friday".

On 20th January 1931 the lantern slides were being finalised for "the reading of the paper on Friday 23rd January" but on the same day, 10000 was in charge of the 1.54pm Pullman turn in charge of driver J. Gascoigne. The new hinged fire door was giving trouble and the reducing valve was still a problem; however, due to defective brakes on the train, the locomotive had to be punished to maintain time "but in spite of this full boiler pressure was maintained and the coal consumption was noticeably light" [I am sorry Inspector Swan (on the footplate) but I simply do not believe it. I think that a bad report three days before the presentation would be frowned upon and the truth was held back.] On the 22nd January 1931, J.H. Smeddle, Locomotive Running Superintendent, did not hold back when he stated "the coal slaking pipe is not of sufficient capacity". Another huge clue! [Note also the correct term "slaking", not "slacking"; it is a slaker (slake – to create a water slurry) pipe not a slacker pipe.] Mr Smeddle also wrote, "The firedoor has been giving trouble owing to being too fine a fit on the bearings, and I have informed Mr Schlegel that he must ease this so that the expansion will not jam the bearings".

The File

On Friday 23rd January 1931, Gresley presented his paper as summarised here.

Gresley, H.N. 1931

"High-pressure locomotives. 101-35. Disc.:135-206 + 3 folding plates. 8 illus., 14 diagrs., 2 tables, 2 plans."

Locomotives described include the Delaware & Hudson two-cylinder compound locomotive of 1924; the Schmidt-Henschel three-cylinder compound locomotive of 1926; the Swiss Winterthur high-pressure locomotive (2-6-2T) of 1927; and the Berlin Machine Works Schwartzkopff-Löffler three-cylinder locomotive of 1930. He then described No. 10000, with its Yarrow boiler.

Discussion: N.H. Scarth (Yarrow); F. Wempe (Schmidt); G. Haffner (Chief Engineer, French State Railways); A.C. Roger (French State Railways); Sir Henry Fowler; R.E.L. Maunsell; W.A. Stanier; E. Kitson Clark; H.A. Stenning Gysel; W.W. Marriner (Yarrow); Charles King; P.J. Cowan; W. Gregson; R.J. Glinn.

The paper was discussed in Manchester on 5th February, Leeds on 12th February (where W.T. Athey stated that he had entered Gateshead as an apprentice in 1887, and commented on compounding and boiler scale) and at a meeting in Glasgow on 18th March: where speakers included Harold E. Yarrow.

The report referred to the French extra-high-pressure, PL241B, 4-cylinder compound high-pressure locomotive of 1929. The German extra- and ultra-high-pressure locomotives: the Henschel H17-206 built in 1925on the Schmidt high-pressure system, and the ultra-high-pressure locomotive H02-1001, built in 1929 to the design of Dr L Löffler Schwarzkopff, which began to run it in 1930. Schwarzkopff were brave enough to guarantee, in the purchase contract, a coal saving of 42% over a standard 01 design.

The ultra-high-pressure locomotive in the UK was mentioned.

The Swiss extra-high-pressure locomotive Eb3/5 was built at Winterthur in 1927. The Swiss Locomotive and Machine Company built this 2-6-2 tank engine at the end of 1927, to the design of Mr Buchli, their chief engineer. Extensive trials were made in Switzerland and Austria. It was also tested on the network of the l'Est in France, where it is said to have inspired the French 232 P-1 high-pressure locomotive. It was claimed that it produced 40% more work for the same fuel than a conventional locomotive, and that 2.25lb of coal and 15lb of water per DHP-hr were used when 800 HP was delivered at the drawbar. During trials, it was

reported that most of the scale was deposited in the feed water heater, but some was formed in the boiler tubes.

The Canadian ultra-high-pressure 2-10-4 compound locomotive of 1931, No 8000, was a three-cylinder compound high-pressure experiment built for the Canadian Pacific Railroad. The Schmidt high-pressure system used a closed circuit of distilled water working at 1,350psi. This transferred heat to a high-pressure section working at 850psi, which in turn supplied the centre cylinder. The exhaust steam from this was mixed with 250psi steam from the low-pressure section and fed the two outside cylinders. The locomotive was built by Angus Shops in 1931 and was the Canadian Pacific's heaviest steam locomotive. It operated on the Mountain Subdivision of the CPR from 1931.

Baldwin No 60000 was a 4-10-2 was built by Baldwin in 1926, and celebrated the construction of their 60,000th locomotive. The water-tube boiler generated steam at 350psi, feeding the central high-pressure cylinder. The exhaust from this fed the two outer low-pressure cylinders. At the Pennsylvania Railroad's Altoona testing facility, 60000 registered 4515 horsepower. It covered 100,000 miles as a demonstrator and then undertook trials in California, making trips over the Donner Summit. 60000 returned to the East in 1927 and was put to use as a stationary power source at Baldwin's Pennsylvania works. 60000 survives as, in 1933, it was installed in the Franklin Institute Science Museum in Philadelphia, Pennsylvania, where it still remains in 2010.

The New York Central No 800, HS-1a of 1931 was a 4-8-4 compound locomotive, an experiment built in 1931 by ALCO for the New York Central Railroad. The boiler generated steam at 850psi to feed the central high-pressure cylinder. The two outer low-pressure cylinders worked at 250psi. After carrying out test runs, it was used as a hump shunter in Selkirk yard.

No 1400 *Horatio Allen* was built in 1924 by the Delaware & Hudson Railroad. The water-tube boiler designed by D&H consultant John Muhlfeld generated steam at 350psi. 1400 was a two-cylinder cross compound with a two-axle booster on the bogie at the rear of the tender. The boiler barrel was conventional, with fire tubes and a superheater, but four steam drums, two at the top and two at the bottom enclosed the firebox. Vertical water tubes connected the top and bottom drums at each side of the firebox. The bottom drums extended only for the length of the firebox, but the top steam drums extended farther forward, over the boiler barrel. There was no transverse tube connection

Above and opposite page, top: Departing Leeds on 7th July 1930. (Ken Hoole Collection)

Opposite page, bottom: Ken Hoole suggests this as Headingly, probably 7th July 1930, and sure enough it looks like the same train that was seen departing Hartlepool and Leeds. (Ken Hoole Collection)

between the two top drums. Young valve gear, which can provide a maximum cut off greater than 90%, was used. The large pipe over the top of the smokebox carried the exhaust from the high-pressure cylinder to the low-pressure cylinder on the other side.

No 1401 *John B Jervis* was built in 1927 by the Delaware & Hudson Railroad. 1401 closely resembled 1400, having a water-tube boiler and a two-axle booster at the rear of the tender. Boiler pressure was higher, at 400psi, and the cylinders were slightly smaller. No 1402 *James Archbald* was built in 1930 by the Delaware & Hudson Railroad. 1402 was a two-cylinder compound with a 500psi water tube boiler. The driving wheels were 63in diameter (illustrated on page 14).

To Continue the 10000 Story

On 26th January 1931, "two copies of all photographs taken of the above engine [10000] during construction, for an album for Mr Gresley" were requested. [Lawrie Loveless has found these at the National Railway Museum, York, during his research for his 0-gauge production model of the W1, as built.]

On 6th February 1931, R.J. Robson wrote to Yarrow & Co, "Confirming telephone conversation this morning, asking Mr Scarth to be present at Gateshead Shed early on Monday morning, as the boiler of the above engine is to be cleaned and examined and made ready for traffic for the following day."

This was to be quite a week for North Road works, although there is little evidence of what transpired following 12th February 1931, the date on which an unprecedented report of three pages from J.N. Gresham regarding "the injector" was produced. Of particular note is: "we do not feel that 1½" pipe from the boiler is sufficiently large to carry the amount of steam required. We ourselves advocate a 1½" steam pipe for a No 9 Injector and a 1¼" steam pipe for the combination Ejector, to say nothing of the other fittings". [No wonder the auxiliaries were failing intermittently. How

Poppleton Junction with the Dynamometer Car. *This is some time in February 1931 around the time of the unprecedented J.N. Gresham report of the 12th. Insufficient auxiliary steam was the problem, and the temporary cure was to be ordered on 9th May 1931. (Ken Hoole Collection)*

embarrassing, after all the letters that changed hands and over one year of trials down the pan. Anyone with footplate experience will tell you that it is quite impossible to safely maintain a full head of steam when the injectors are unreliable. The pressure has to be backed off until they co-operate. Hush-Hush would not work on a rolling chassis entirely due to lack of auxiliary steam! It must have been doubly embarrassing for Gresley as he had pointed out the neat arrangement of the auxiliaries manifold in his paper and unknown to him it did not work!]

Throughout March and April 1931, the only letters in the file refer to a problem with automatic coupling on the curve in Newcastle Central Station, which was common with all of the corridor tenders, weighing of the locomotive, and the requests for photographs. One in letter in particular, from Gresley to Stamer, seems to capture the mood. "I am returning to you under separate cover the book of photographs of the above engine, and shall be glad if you will arrange for these to be put in a proper album." [Gresley must have been feeling that they couldn't even produce a decent album for the boss, but he determined that they will get it

right. I wonder who got the blame for the woeful arrangements for the auxiliary steam, which must have ranked as a fundamental schoolboy error. If there were any letters changing hands they must have been vitriolic enough to be removed from the records.]

Finally, on 9th May 1931, Gresley wrote to Stamer, "Confirming conversation yesterday, will you kindly arrange to fit independent steam supply to the H.P. injector and bronze die blocks" and by 18th May the drawings for the supply had been prepared, sent to Yarrows, for their approval, and approval given. On 22nd May, Gresley wrote to Stamer, "I should like to have another copy of this album for Mr Yarrow." [Is this the second one at York?]

North Road had run out of 1½in pipe and on 29th May 1931, "this pipe is required immediate, as we want to alter the engine as soon as it comes back from Glasgow." [There is no reference in the file as to why it went to Glasgow, or any other evidence that it in fact did, but this might account for the ***apparent*** delay of almost three months in responding to the revelation.]

On 5th June 1931, a communication was issued: "No. 10000 Engine Headed Poster ... showing

Above: Probably at Stratford. *10000 was making its way to the Norwich Exhibition on 1ˢᵗ May 1931. (Ken Hoole Collection)*

Right: Norwich on 2ⁿᵈ May 1931. *The sign suggests that the W1 represents dignity in this view. I have to say that, up to this point, there would have been nothing dignified about the comments of the firemen, fitters and others. The problem with the auxiliaries was being sorted out, albeit on a temporary basis. Events behind the scenes at the LNER were well masked. (Ken Hoole Collection)*

The W1 leaves Norwich in the company of "Flying Scotsman". (Ken Hoole Collection)

At last we have a picture of a fully functioning W1. *The problems with the auxiliaries were cured and the locomotive was at last fit for purpose. 10000 is seen here at Middlesbrough on 5th July 1931. (Ken Hoole Collection)*

The File

It must have been a delight for the driver and fireman to arrive at the capital with a fully functioning machine.
Ken Hoole suggests that this photograph could have been taken on either the 20th, 22nd or 24th July 1931 at Kings Cross. (Ken Hoole Collection)

particulars of painting … The colour is made of lead colour in paste with a small addition of common black paste mixed with varnish and turpentine. The makers of the lead colour are: - Messrs. Kersley [Kearsley] & Co. Ripen. [Ripon] Yorks." The new *Flying Scotsman* publicity had 10000 in charge. [A Flying Scotsman booklet was published with 10000 on the front but as for the poster?] Such was the new confidence in this machine. However we must not go overboard as this machine was designed to be equivalent in output to the A1 and would have to play catch-up to be as powerful as the new A3 and the A1 rebuilds.

On 24th June 1931, a representative of Davies and Metcalf was requested for the steaming of Friday 26th instant, "so that the L.P. injector can be tried". The same invitation was given to Gresham & Craven "so that the H.P. injector can be tried".

On 8th September 1931, following a trial on the 4th it was found that the relief valve on the low-pressure cylinder was blowing off at 180psi: "will you please have these adjusted in accordance with the drawing, i.e. to blow off at 220lbs per sq. Inch." Notice that by now

this was working as a mimic for a three-cylinder machine. In the reports of previous working, with four cylinders, the low-pressure steam chest, and hence cylinders, got nowhere near 180psi, let alone 220. [Should the setting to 220psi have followed from the increase to 450psi in the design stage?] Now 10000 was indeed playing catch-up and must have been using full gear in the high-pressure cylinders to get the 180psi plus in the low-pressure cylinders. More evidence of the catch-up was the order and supply of a new No 10 injector to replace the No 9, which by now had been through the wars in the hands of frustrated fitters.

On 18th September 1931, diagram No 14663.D. *Tank for Sodium Aluminate Water Softener* was passed to the works "to have this fitted". On 23rd September, instructions were given to, "take out the cylinders of engine 10,000 and arrange for welding up the defective parts". By 25th November, the front hinged plate was missing. During November and December 1931, Gresham & Craven carried out maintenance and supplied new cones for the equipment in their supply.

The hinged front plate had been dispensed with by the time this shot was taken on 25th November 1931. The running department must have found this inconvenient and, as 10000 was now a workaday machine, it was removed, or maybe it was simply left off at the last works visit? (Ken Hoole Collection)

Phase 4: Fit For Purpose

[1932 had arrived and a new year of working with 10000. The number of documents remaining to explore has reduced considerably. It is of note that the vast majority of the file, to this point, consists of letters drafted as a result of the LNER's failure to supply sufficient auxiliary steam, which must have been a source of embarrassment for Gresley. The locomotive is now effectively running as a three-cylinder compound, the two high-pressure cylinders working in unison, albeit at 90 degrees apart, nominally 450psi high pressure and 220psi low. Again there are reports that 10000 was no better than a good standard Pacific, but we have established that the locomotive was constrained to be no better, in terms of haulage, than a standard Pacific. Therefore to be "no better than a ***good*** standard Pacific" is in fact a huge compliment. It was one of the good ones. We should also bear in mind, as has been stated earlier, that North Road was 10000's home depot, and reports of being "in works" are in some cases, unreliable. The machine was often at home for routine tasks in line with what were, or were intended to be, normal shed practices. We have also established that the running side expected a machine that would be subject to normal day-to-day maintenance and objected to "non-routine" activities. Opposed to this was Gresley, using the machine as a test bed, often unavailable due to the necessary, but time-consuming, setting up for trials.]

I find only one letter in January 1932, and this relates to the supply of cones. In February, modifications to the fire door and weighing of the locomotive were the only references, and in March, 10in piston rings and a set of springs were to be set aside for spares. In April, several drawings were brought up to date and minor changes to the flue casings were drafted.

On 20th April 1932, the results of tests on "the model of the flue working" were outlined. Several baffle arrangements were tried, one of which was longitudinal and had been proposed by Mr Stedman, the running Superintendent at York: "Whilst gasses could be made to go the path desired, it was not altogether satisfactory, and Mr Gresley eventually ruled the arrangement out."

On 21st April, temporary repairs to a combustion chamber panel were outlined in order that 10000 could travel to Harwich for an exhibition on the 28th.

22nd April, "His [Gresley's] suggestion is to make the flue casing in one panel and to make provision somewhat in the lines indicated, thus reducing the number of joints in the casing to a minimum". [I can't help thinking that it was a sad state of affairs that the locomotive had been given over one year of serious abuse and had gone through what must have amounted to ten years worth of thermal cycling due to the failure of the auxiliaries, yet only now be in a position to do the job. All of the consequent maintenance problems were stacking up against the locomotive, for no good reason.]

By 23rd May 1932: "It would be advantageous if the engine as it now stands, without making any further alteration, with the exception of arranging the baffles, and bricking up of the tubes, and removing the brick arch as shown on print No 15006.D was put into traffic for a week or so, we would then be able to see whether the alteration to the baffling and the brickwork was showing any improvement. I suggest this more to gain experience before making any alteration to the outer casing, superheater and elements." Also on this date, a Memo for Mr Stamer outlined drawing enclosures of proposed changes to the outer casing L/32, H/32, flue J/32, P/32, Q/32, combustion chamber K/32, superheater 15006.D, and baffle plates 15007.D, 15008.D, and a list of tests carried out:

Test No 1   As the engine is at present fitted
Test No 2   Mr. Gresley
Test No 3   Mr. Marriner
Test No 4   Messrs. Yarrow
Test No 5   Mr. Horwill

Evidence of Gresley further investigating water-tube boilers, no doubt for the next step, came on 27th May 1932: "After discussing the boiler casing problems, he produced the drawing of the Swiss High Pressure Locomotive which he had previously discussed with Mr Marriner at York on March 20th last. Mr Gresley asked me for the smallest size of water drum for three rows of tubes. The drums shown on the boiler were about 8″ diameter with only one row of tubes, approximately 3″ diameter reduced to about 1½″ diameter at the water drums."

[An LNER diagram shows a K3 with a water-tube boiler pressed to 300psi. This diagram, produced in July 1931,would have followed the discussion of 20th March that year, mentioned earlier, and clearly picked up again in 1932 after 10000 was proven fit for purpose. Almost certainly a three-cylinder compound, Gresley having proved that this would indeed work; the height of the proposed machine was exactly the same as 10000: 12ft 11in. The author mentions severe cut backs in construction in 1932/3. The extra-high-pressure K3 had to wait, or go elsewhere for development.]

By the end of May 1932, work was in hand to make permanent alterations and, needless to say, something of all of the proposals was incorporated, including longitudinal baffles, "to increase the velocity of gasses at this part of the flue, and the test certainly showed this increase in velocity". R.J. Robson wrote to the Works Manager, Darlington, on 7th June 1932: "I presume Mr. Stamer has already arranged with you to bring the engine into the works and have the outer casing completely removed, and the flue casing started with as early as possible, to Dgs. Nos. 15033.D. & 15034.D." Letters were then exchanged in respect to

drawings, obtaining materials, and troubleshooting these modifications.

The problem with auxiliary steam supply had not entirely gone away and thoughts moved on to a permanent solution to auxiliary demand. On 11th June 1932, R.J. Robson wrote to Davies & Metcalfe, "in connection with the L.P. injector and Ejector, which are fitted to the above engine. It is proposed to use the ejector for H.P. steam, 450lbs".

On 15th June 1932, buckled plates were removed. The tubes exposed were found to be in good order.

On 17th June 1932, Davies & Metcalfe propose a 450psi ejector and by 21st June: "Attached is Dg. No.15076.D. shewing the L.P. Injector and Ejector which were originally operated from the manifold. They are now operated with H.P. steam, 450lbs". The manifold for the auxiliaries was to be dispensed and remaining auxiliary equipment proposed to be run on steam at 450lbs. A communication on 21st June outlined the modifications required to facilitate this. The suppliers indicated that modifying it to suit 450lbs was not a problem with straightforward changes. Several letters changed hands during June and July in this respect on a troubleshooting basis.

On 7th July 1932, a letter to Stamer from Gresley outlined a proposal from Messrs Yarrow & Co Ltd: "Now that the casings are taken off the boiler, all the tubes are exposed and we would recommend for their future preservation that they are sprayed with ordinary coal tar on the outside; especially we would recommend their being coated at the tube plates. We ourselves always do this with our marine boilers as we find that it delays corrosion. There is no harm done if some of the tar gets on the tubes in a place where they have to transmit heat as in these places the tar very soon burns away". "I [Gresley] shall be glad if you will arrange this in accordance with Messrs. Yarrow's recommendation." Yarrow & Co had despatched the spray gear and tar mixture to Darlington by the 9th July.

On 11th July 1932: "Referring to the Chief Loco. Draughtsman's visit to your [Gresley's] office on Thursday last, with reference to reverting to the 12″ dia. H.P. Cylinders". [Whilst I find no written instruction or associated drawing to revert to 12in, it can be deduced that this was carried out. During the October/November 1932 trials the high-pressure piston rings failed and the order for replacements used the original 12in piston drawings, one set during the trials and one after. This arrangement, of course, approximated to an even torque across all four cylinders and a resulting higher power output, but made it difficult to identify thermal efficiency improvements

Springfield on 3rd September 1932. By the time this photograph was taken, a permanent solution to the auxiliary steam supply had been found, that is, 450psi to the injectors, from the boiler rather than the manifold; there was no trouble in producing a full head of steam on demand. *(Ken Hoole Collection)*

The locomotive was required for an exhibition at Hull Dairycoates. This view, taken on or around 15th October 1933, clearly shows the new bracket associated with the screw reverse that had been fitted. Notice the North Eastern Atlantic behind. *(Ken Hoole Collection)*

A view of Hush Hush taken in 1933. (Ken Hoole Collection)

against the standard A3 Pacific, which had three.]

By 23rd August 1932, all auxiliaries with the exception of the motor generator were converted to 450psi and the locomotive scheduled to be steamed on Friday morning, the 26th. The locomotive was duly weighed on the 25th in preparation of a new set of trials.

[There are no records in the file of trial runs with the "three-cylinder equivalent" arrangement after the problem with the auxiliary supply was identified and either temporarily or permanently rectified. The reversion to 12in occurred at the same time as the permanent solution to the auxiliaries was carried out. I suspect, however, that satisfactory information was assimilated as a certain French gentleman, reputedly a good friend of Gresley, was to produce the astounding 2-4-2A1 with the 90+135+135 three-cylinder compound arrangement that 10000 had been set up to test, albeit as an approximation only. Incidentally I have found no correspondence or record of any communication between Gresley and André Chapelon in the file. It seems, from other sources, that Bulleid was the man at Vitry, with 2001. It has to be said that Gresley must have seen Chapelon on several occasions including, for example, the international railway conferences.]

2nd September 1932, and a report was issued, "Engine No 10000".

As part of the modifications to the casing, much of the brickwork had been replaced and the fallen firebrick, which clearly did not cause sufficient concern to stop the locomotive, was not a serious issue. The changes to the auxiliaries, whilst individually relatively minor, had been significant and these worked "right first time". [The down side to the test was the use of compounding. For almost all the first half of the 20th Century incorrect conclusions from testing of compounds had resulted in the belief that, as Gresley put it: "I have always understood that the most efficient way of running a compound is to fix the L.P. cut off and adjust to demand by varying the H.P." This was, subsequently, proven to be quite wrong by André Chapelon who was to run compounds with spectacular results using the method of full charge in the high-pressure cylinder and varying the low-pressure to adjust to demand, which had been another, less powerful, school of thought. Notice that the best balance on these results was when the high-pressure cut off was significantly longer than the low-pressure. The cut off in the high-pressure cylinders was as much as 90% in full gear. Analysis of the data relating to the set up of the double Kylchap (K.C.) blastpipe reveals that Hush-Hush would have pulled 3960 horsepower at 90% cut

off in the high-pressure cylinders.]

On 8th September 1932: "Mr. R.J. Robson's report on running of Engine No. 10000 from Newcastle to Edinboro' 12.22pm. and Edinboro' to Newcastle 5.17pm. (Fish). Driver, G. Morton, Fireman, J. Bambra, Mr R.J. Robson, Inspector Dick on footplate." The only significance of this test was that it was now proved to consistently produce a full head of steam, but the working of the compound engines was, again, woeful. [So much for the extra-high-pressure boiler not working on a rolling chassis, the real problem, after putting the auxiliaries right, was how the compound engines were operated.]

The auxiliaries were not perfect; however they did at least work in a similar fashion to the ones on the standard Pacific, the key to good working being cleanliness. The firebricks misbehaved from time to time, just as in the standard Pacifics with their brick arches.

A series of tests were carried out, one on 17th October 1932 where "a slight leakage was noticed at of one of the doors" and it was thought prudent to put the locomotive on normal duties for a fortnight before recommencing the trials. It is strange that, on 27th October, a set of high-pressure piston rings were ordered, with no evidence of them being fitted. Trials restarted on 31st October, but, it was reported, the piston rings failed on the last day. New ones were ordered immediately after the 5th November, and by then the trials had ended. [I suppose it could be argued that it is a coincidence that after the first day someone realised that there were no spare piston rings and ordered some and then these were almost immediately used and replaced. The events are somewhat confusing.]

The remainder of 1932 seems to have been uneventful, as far as the file is concerned, and communication consisted of requests for, and despatch of, various drawings for information only. On 13th January 1933 the paperweight issue reappeared and from the letter it seems that this had yet to be produced: "Messrs. Britains Ltd, who made the latter [Flying Scotsman] model, has offered to produce a similar one of Locomotive No 10,000 at a price which will enable us to sell it at 2/6d the price of the 'Flying Scotsman' model". More drawings were issued for this purpose. This time it was manufactured. One can be seen at the National Railway Museum. I have the later Silver Link paperweight of the same series.

There are no documents in the file for the period 18th August 1933 to 5th September 1934 and even after this date there were not many. My commentary

A Low fell on 27th September 1934. Exactly 109 years after the opening of the S&DR. (Ken Hoole Collection)

Still with the single blastpipe but for not much longer. Here the locomotive is on display at the York Exhibition, 14th October 1934. (Ken Hoole Collection)

By 6th March 1935 the double blastpipe had been drafted and instructions for this to be fitted issued. By the time this view at Hunslet goods yard had been taken on 12th May 1935 it was in place. (Ken Hoole Collection)

continues with considerable gaps in time.

A.C. Stamer had retired at the end of 1933 to be replaced by Edward Thompson. Stamer's job of Assistant Chief Mechanical Engineer lapsed at this time, and Thompson became Mechanical Engineer North East Area, at Darlington.

The first mention of fitting a double blastpipe and chimney was in a letter from Thompson to the Locomotive Drawing Office, dated 6th September 1934, where, "Mr. Gresley is considering the question of fitting a double blast pipe and chimney". By 6th March 1935, the drawings of the (double) "K.C." blast pipe had been produced, and a note was sent to E. Thompson Esq: "Will you kindly arrange for engine No. 10,000 to be modified in accordance with these drawings. [signed] H.N.Gresley"

On 10th May 1935, Thompson wrote to The Mechanical Engineer, Doncaster: "The Chief Mechanical Engineer informs me that he has made some modification in connection with the firebars of engine No. 2001, as a result of the Vitry experiments and he is anxious that this should be applied to engine No. 10,000".

26th May 1935: "Counter Pressure Tests Leeds and Hull

"The Chief Mechanical Engineer desires to make tests with engine 10,000 and engine 761 working between Leeds and Hull, Wednesday May 29th. Engine [761] and Dynamometer car will run from North road works to Neville Hill Shed via Ripon. Tests were carried out to find the effect of different combinations." This refers to the correct setting up of the double K.C. blastpipe as this could only be determined by experiment. "After the completion of the tests on Thursday, 6th June, engine 10,000 will remain at Leeds Neville Hill Shed." One striking element of the test is that the safety valves must have been reset to at least 475psi. On several occasions the recorded pressure was 475psi, which must have been deliberate; otherwise the test would have been halted due to safety valve failure.

10000, the dynamometer car and counter pressure Class S, all on Ripon Viaduct. For me this is the most exciting shot of 10000 possible. Stephen Middleton, of the wonderful Stately Trains, is pretty sure that his father took it, and just by chance. His desperation to capture the moment would account for the slight lack of focus. Fantastic! (Stephen Middleton/Ken Hoole Collection)

The compound settings were no better than before, but were explored in a more rigorous way. The cut off in the high-pressure cylinders was increased in steps 30%, 40% and 50% and for low-pressure 25%, 35%, 45% and 55%, in all combinations, but there is no evidence that anything came of it other than to set up the blastpipe. See Appendix C for the test results. [Analysis of this data reveals that if the W1 had been run with 90% cut off in the high-pressure cylinders, the drawbar horsepower would have been just short of 4000!]

The last letter in the file was written on 14th September 1935 and referred to overheating in the cab.

Above: At Hunslet goods yard.
This picture shows another view of this developing machine, where again the double chimney can be seen. (Ken Hoole Collection)

Left: 10000 passes Ripon on 17th May 1935. It was too late in the day to fit the "British Enterprise" nameplates, even though it was by now the equal of a good A3 Pacific. (Ken Hoole Collection)

At Newcastle station. The double chimney can be seen clearly. (Ken Hoole Collection)

Newcastle, 18ᵗʰ May 1935. This unusual view shows 10000 waiting to take the 4 17 pm to Liverpool via West Hartlepool. (Ken Hoole Collection)

Passing Stockton North Shore in 1935. *This is the only view of 10000 taken from a train that I have seen. (Ken Hoole Collection)*

Neville Hill Motive Power Depot July 1935 with smoke lifting cowl fitted. *By now the boiler had been pressed to 475psi but sadly, according to the record, not in ideal compound mode (long cut off in the high pressure and control for demand with the low). Maybe the receiver had insufficient capacity, a large receiver is needed for this way of working to be fully effective. (Ken Hoole Collection)*

Stooperdale Paint Shop Yard, 1935.
Left: *This grey image certainly gives one the feel that the days of working extra-high pressure are over. This must have been in August 1935 as it was in store in the paint shop by the 21ˢᵗ.*
Right: *Not pending a decision to fit a P2 boiler, but waiting its turn to go into Doncaster works to become the most powerful passenger locomotive to run in the British Isles. We now know that it could have been achieved with the water-tube boiler and revised inside-cylinder arrangements. Gresley died before Chapelon proved that this could be done, with the machine set up the way Gresley had planned in the first place! (Ken Hoole Collection)*

I hope that the file has equipped you with enough facts to enable accurate judgements about this machine. In this respect I can offer a couple of typical commentaries that can be reviewed by the reader in an entirely new light.

The Northern Echo Rail 150
August 1975
Page 10, J.W. Armstrong looks back to the 1920s...

"A visit to the works [Darlington, North Road] revealed that something unusual was on the way. The guide pointed out a locomotive chassis all sheeted up in a corner of the new pits. 'That's our Hush-Hush job', he said laughingly

"And that was the name that stuck to the monster throughout her working life.

"The night of December 6 had a pleasant surprise. Going home from work, I noticed that the paint shop and yard were fully illuminated, most unusual in those days of strict economy. In the gloom I could hear the familiar sound of a dead engine being propelled, air whistling out of the cylinder taps. Then I saw a mighty grey shape with the number 10000 on the cab side, ready for the final finish to the paintwork.

Black Smoke
"She was soon ready for steaming, and never since No.1 [Locomotion, 1825] had an engine made such an impact on the town. The local Press hailed it in a manner more fitting to a film star, and a local tobacconist brought out a Hush-Hush pipe mixture.

"But she was troubled by bad steaming, and I saw her one night at Bank Top [station, Darlington] working the 1.20 p.m. from Kings Cross, the afternoon Scotsman, with the usual heavy load plus dynamometer car.

"The train was due about 5.42 p.m. but the telegraph board told the sad story of time lost.

"Doncaster, York and Northallerton, all showed arrears adding up and she finally crawled along No 4 platform, well behind time, with her crew of driver Jack Eltringham and fireman Slinger and an inspector in grimy condition.

"As soon as she had stopped, the staff were up to the cab where the pressure gauge told its sorry tale. After a brief consultation, the driver and fireman set to and started to clean the fire, to try to get the old girl to boil.

"It is essential with a compound engine for the boiler pressure always to be near maximum, whereas a simple engine can scrape through on a low pressure.

"The people of Pensbury Street got the full result of fireman Slinger's efforts. Volumes of black smoke issued from 10000. Eventually it was decided a start could be made, and she slowly got under way. For the first time in my long observations at Bank Top, the main line pilot was giving rear assistance out of the platform to make sure she got going.

"There had been many suggestions as to what name should be bestowed on 10000, with letters in the local Press quoting *British Enterprise*, Darlington and others. No doubt the two Gateshead lads on the footplate had some appropriate titles for her."

The Locomotives of Sir Nigel Gresley

O.S.Nock, B.Sc., D.I.C., A.M.Inst.C.E., M.I.Mech.E., A.I.Loco.E.
Compiled from articles appearing in *The Railway Magazine* 1941, 1942, 1943 with some revisions and additions, 1945

"While the Super-Pacific design was being developed, a still larger engine was under construction at Darlington, the 4-cylinder compound 4-6-4 No. 10000. The first appearance of this unique locomotive at the close of 1929, little more than a year after the 'A3s' had come out, may have given rise to ideas that the two designs were in some way connected: that the trial of 450lb.per sq. In. pressure in No 10000 was a sequel to the success of the previous moderate increase, from the 180 lb. of the 'A1s' to the 220 lb. of the 'A3s'.

Actually, however, the conception of a high-pressure locomotive design dates back to almost pre-grouping days, and was unaffected by any current events on the L.N.E.R. In a paper read before the Institution of Mechanical Engineers on January 23, 1931, Gresley tells that he was so impressed by the striking increases of efficiency obtained in land and marine boilers by the use of high steam pressures that he began to formulate a design of locomotive which it was hoped would realise the same advantages. By 1924 his own ideas were sufficiently advanced for him, in September of that year, to approach Mr. Harold Yarrow, of Glasgow, with a view to the latter's firm building a high-pressure boiler of the water tube type suitable for a locomotive...
"...During the summer of 1930 she was working on the ordinary Gateshead Pacific link, including the long-mileage double-manned turn, beginning with the 11.17 a.m. from Newcastle to Edinburgh; this latter [later in the day] included the 43-minute Darlington-York run of the evening Glasgow-Leeds dining car express. Mr R.A.H.Weight timed her from Darlington to York, 44.1 miles, at exactly 60 m.p.h. from start to stop with a load of 440 tons. On July 31, 1930 she worked the Flying Scotsman non-stop from Edinburgh to Kings Cross, returning on the corresponding train next day; I witnessed her arrival on the up journey, dead on time. In general performance, however, the early promise of success was not realised, and No. 10000 proved a troublesome engine to maintain; but although posterity will remember her best in her rebuilt form as a giant in the noble regiment of blue streamliners, the boldness of the original conception, and the superb engineering put into her construction must not be lightly dismissed."

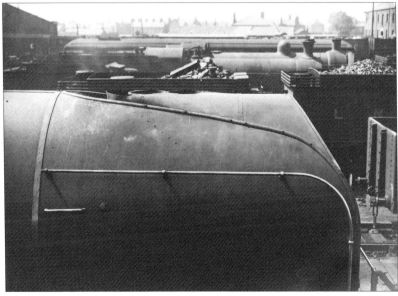

Close up of cowl in 1935. I have seen a similar view of a Bulleid Pacific in one of the modified states, and the similarity is striking. Taken at North Road Yard, with sister sentinel in the background. (Ken Hoole Collection)

CHAPTER 3

The Rebuild and the Final Years

We now know the origins of Hush-Hush and the events during its lifetime as water tube and compound. It would be remiss of me to leave this work without looking at events after August 1935. We will look at the motive power Gresley was developing concurrently with the water-tube locomotive and the machines that consequently followed, up to his untimely demise. Some post-dated projects elsewhere, of a related nature, will also be covered. Then we will look at the work that 10000 had a direct influence upon, that is, Sentinel, Leader, and Chapelon's 2-4-2A1 and projected designs. Finally we will look at 21st century developments.

While No 10000 was in for repairs, No 2509 exceeded 100mph on what was to be a scheduled train. The impact was immediate, and must rank alongside the launch of the first space shuttle in terms of importance. The LNER publicity department was keen to take advantage of this: the new contest for speed was well and truly back on, and the LNER was winning the race.

The saving in horse power, and resulting payback, from streamlining starts at about 100mph, and only the A4s were doing this routinely. However, the popular understanding of "state of the art" was represented by the newer art-deco "Buggatti" front end, and therefore it made perfect sense, to the publicity department, to put this on every top-link locomotive, and so it did. This process was purely as a status symbol for the sub-100mph locomotives, to attract more, and wealthier, customers to produce a good return on investment. The proposed streamlining of the V2s was, in this scenario, a complete non-starter as, with no guarantee that any of the V2s would be restricted to premier trains, seen on a freight train, the image could be destroyed.

The rebuilt 10000. *On Kings Cross Station turntable. (Ken Hoole Collection)*

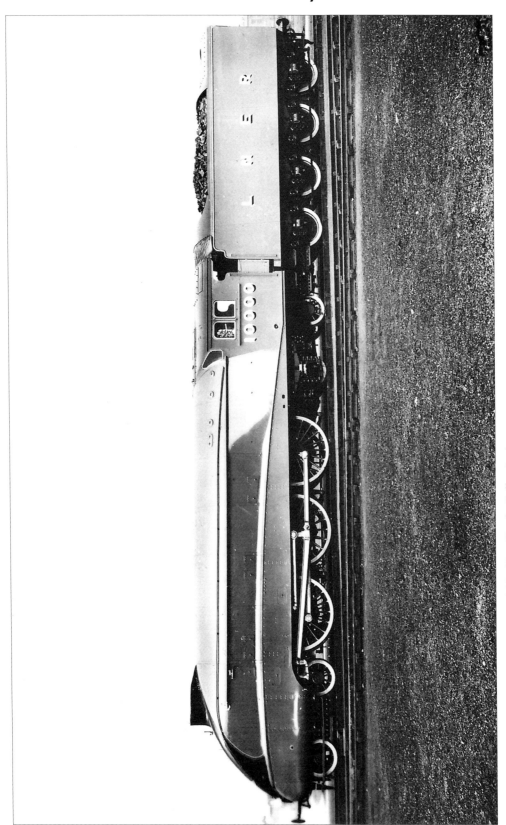

The rebuilt 10000 ex-works. Doncaster 1937. (Ken Hoole Collection)

The Rebuild and the Final Years

At that time, contrary to popular opinion, 10000 was awaiting its turn in the workshops, and was not "laid aside". The plans for its rebuild began to be drawn up virtually as soon as the speed record was set. The rebuilds were to be facilitated in order of difficulty, easiest first, of course. The timetable was:

10000	Repairs Darlington. Not repaired, standing in the paint shop, 21st August 1935.
2509	Introduced 6th September 1935.
2509	First 100mph run with streamlined train on 27th September 1935.
10000	Drawing 16431 by 2nd January 1936, arrangement showing P2 boiler fitted to engine No 10000.
2003	To traffic June 1936.
2004	To traffic July 1936.
2005	To traffic August 1936.
2006	To traffic September 1936.
2002	Restyled only, to traffic October 1936.
10000	To Doncaster for rebuild 13th October 1936.
2859	Restyled, to traffic September 1937, B17.
2870	Restyled, to traffic September 1937, B17.
2001	To works for rebuild September 1937.

After commencing the design of W1, Gresley also worked on the following projects:

1927	During the design and build work with 10000. The Kitson Still 2-6-2SD was trialled.
1930	Fitted booster to S1. V1. Y10 Super Sentinel.
1931	H1 rebuilt to A8. C7 rebuilt to C9, booster fitted, 4-4-2-6.

The rebuilt 10000. On shed. (Ken Hoole Collection)

10000 hauls tourist stock. (Ken Hoole Collection)

Rebuild at Hadley Wood 31st July 1948. *By now, the valances had been removed and the W1 has become British Railways 60700, the unnamed streak. I understand that the locomotive was to be named "Pegasus" and that the plates were cast. It has been said that the nameplates lay in Doncaster Works Yard for many years. (Ken Hoole Collection)*

| 1932 | Armstrong Whitworth 0-6-0DE was on trial with the LNER. Armstrong Whitworth Railcars. | 1937 | K4. |

1932   Armstrong Whitworth 0-6-0DE was on trial with the LNER.
Armstrong Whitworth Railcars.

1933   Armstrong Whitworth 2-6-2DE was on trial with the LNER.
Armstrong Whitworth Lightweight Railcar.

1934   P2.

1935   A4.

1936   V2.
Gresley was knighted, made honorary DSC, Manchester University and became President of the Institution of Mechanical Engineers.

1937   K4.

1939   V3.

1941   V4 with thermic siphon.
EM1 Electric.
Sir Nigel Gresley dies.

Edward Thompson, Gresley's replacement, was to use the rebuilt 10000 in trials, during 1941, to prove the rebuild of the P2s to Pacifics. Thompson must have been quite happy with the 10000 rebuild to use it for proving purposes, being used as a target standard, although he was to replace derived drive with inside valve gear in the rebuilt P2s. The first of the P2s to be rebuilt was during 1941 and the remainder were rebuilt

In 1941 the water tube boiler was installed at Stooperdale boiler works. Here it went on to serve as a stationary boiler for a further 24 years. The boiler gave a staggering 30 years of continuous service with little renewal of parts when compared to the standard boiler. (Ken Hoole Collection)

when the war, for many but sadly not everyone, was all but over in 1944. In 1941, the extra-high-pressure boiler was installed as a steam generator at Stooperdale Works, Darlington, where it was to continue in use until the works closed in 1965. By the late 1940s the Sentinels were in decline.

In 1951, 60700 (as 10000 had by then been renumbered) was targeted for withdrawal, being non-standard. It was argued that it was standard in respect to the individual parts, for example a Peppercorn type, if required, could easily replace the boiler and the chassis was common in most respects to the A3. The bogie was the same as the B17. It survived for that important Doncaster – Kings Cross turn. Later, in spite of the bogie failure and the consequent derailment at Peterborough, 10000 soldiered on (see pages 92 to 94). But in 1959, all non-standard locomotives were again targeted for elimination. On this occasion there was no reprieve.

60700 was finally withdrawn in 1959. The water tube boiler lasted six years longer, continuing to steam until 1965, stationary, at Stooperdale. The original tender, with 10000 for the whole of the LNER period and six months into Nationalisation, eventually held as spare I understand, was privately acquired, along with 60009, and continues to work to this day.

Newcastle 1938. (Ken Hoole Collection)

This page and next: *A series of views of the aftermath of the Peterborough derailment on 1ˢᵗ September 1955.* *(Ken Hoole Collection)*

Peterborough derailment. Hush-Hush was built at the same time as the B17, and consequently received the same design bogie. Maybe this escaped the attention of the works, but it is alleged that, in spite of standing instructions to the contrary, the worn plates on 10000's bogie were built up with weld in a hurry to return the locomotive to service and that the accident illustrated here was the result. In spite of this accident 10000 was returned to service. (Ken Hoole Collection)

Other Developments with High-Pressure and Compound Locomotives

Final Developments on the Delaware & Hudson Railroad

No 1403 was named after the D&H president of thirty-one years, L. F. Loree, and was the only locomotive built in the USA in 1933. This was the fourth locomotive of the D&H extra-high-pressure series. It was a triple-expansion engine with a water-tube boiler. The large pipe visible below the boiler carried the steam from the superheater header to the high-pressure cylinder. The boiler was a water-tube design working at 500psi, the steam feeding a high-pressure cylinder under the right side of the cab, then an intermediate-pressure (IP) cylinder under the left of the cab, and finally the two low-pressure cylinders at the front. Both front and rear cylinders acted on the second driving axle. The low-pressure exhaust went out through the chimney blast pipe as usual. Dabeg poppet valves were fitted, driven by rotary cams. The rotary drive to the rear poppet valves ran backwards and slightly upwards from the second driver. The rear of the tender was carried by a 6-wheel Bethlehem "Auxiliary Locomotive" (or booster), which operated at the full boiler pressure of 500psi to give extra effort for starting. Details of this locomotive can be found on Douglas Self's useful website, as mentioned earlier, at www.dself.dsl.pipex.com.

The Final Baltimore & Ohio Machines

1934   *Lady Baltimore* water-tube 4-4-4 with 84in drivers.
1936   5360 Class V-4 water-tube 4-6-4.
1937   *George H. Emerson* water-tube 4-4-4-4.

For pictures and details of these locomotives see *B&O Power* by Lawrence W. Sagle.

Brotan Boilers in Germany, 1940

In 1940 the need for a powerful locomotive with an axle load of about 18 tonnes became evident. Many lines could take an 18 tonne loading, but not the 20 tonnes of the existing Class 44 locomotive. The result was the BR 42, a 1'E (2-10-0) machine for heavy haulage, and design work was complete by December 1942. Two BR 42 prototypes were fitted with Brotan boilers, potentially providing a weight saving of 3 tonnes, a saving of 500 man-hours manufacturing time, and giving longer permissible periods between boiler maintenance. Locomotives BR 50 3011 and 50 3012 were also built as Brotans, and it was intended to use

them in more 50s and 42s. On the Eastern Front maintenance was sporadic and water quality abysmal, impossible conditions for water tube boilers, therefore no more were built.

La Mont Boiler

Prototype T22571: German State Railway H45 024, 2-10-2, built in 1951. This had a La Mont boiler, with water-tubes with pumped circulation, running at a pressure of 750 psi (42 kp/sq cm). It was intended for heavy freight trains. Based on a class 45 freight engine built by the Reichsbahn in 1941 the H45 024 was fired with brown coal dust and had a condensing tender. It had three cylinders, like the standard class 45, but was compound. The inside cylinder (high-pressure) had a diameter of 400mm, the diameter of the low-pressure cylinder was 520mm. Only two test runs were made, both of which had to be stopped after a few kilometres. Dismantled in 1961, some parts were used with streamlined tank 61002 to produce the high speed GDR Pacific 18201 that runs to this day.

Extra-High Pressure and High-Speed Motors

The 232.P.1 was ordered in 1936, and completed in 1939. This loco was built by the SACM Graffenstaden Company at the time the SNCF was formed. It had a dual-pressure boiler. Water from the tender passed through an ACFI feed water heater, being raised to 215°F. Scale was to be deposited in the low-pressure boiler, keeping it out of the high-pressure water tubes where it would be highly dangerous. The forward low-pressure section worked at 20 Bar, (approximately 300 psi). Hot water was supplied via dual Knorr pumps to the high-pressure boiler at the rear. The high-pressure boiler worked at 60 Bar (approximately 900 psi). The two Knorr high-pressure feed pumps were a special tandem compound design to deal with the high delivery pressure. A Thermix injector bypassed the ACFI feed water heater and delivered straight into the low-pressure boiler. Each driving axle was powered by two high-speed three-cylinder double-acting Uniflow steam engines, which shared a gearbox that gave provision for vertical movement of the wheels. In 1937 the Baltimore & Ohio began to build a locomotive on similar lines, an impressive looking bullet nosed streamliner with water-tube boiler. It was a 4-2-2-2-2-4 with four flat-four high-speed engines. The project was abandoned by 1939. By 1941, Henschel had built a 2-2-2-2-2-2, works number 25000, running number 191001. This had four Vee 2 motors, one for each axle, two alternate on the left and two alternate on the right. This locomotive ended up in the USA after the war and was dismantled, along with others taken over, in 1951/2.

Sentinel

When I was apprentice at Shildon Works, the body of Royal Sovereign was grounded near the level crossing at the entrance of the works. Not to be confused with the Tyneside electric trailer car E29388E that was on its wheels in the sidings near the station. This Sentinel had a Woolnough boiler, which was basically a miniature Yarrow/Gresley. From 1928, the Woolnough boiler with pressure of up to 550psi, was installed in the more powerful Sentinels, shunters, railcars and main line locomotives including the twin railcar *Phenomena*. S.E. Alley, Director, The Sentinel Waggon Works Ltd had patented this at more or less the same time as the Yarrow/Gresley, and the similarity of the construction details are obvious. Was Gresley consultant to Sentinel in producing this? A few clues to this can be found in *Master Builders of Steam*, by H.A.V. Bulleid, and it begins with H.A. Ivatt:

"Ivatt recognised that under such circumstances (where specifications could not be fully detailed) it is useless to build up more and more details and clauses in a specification; far better to get close to your technical "opposite number" in the suppliers organisation and agree the common goal..." (p26)

"The circumstances of the 1910s were entirely different from those of the 1960s in that industry, particularly the railways, had virtually no middle level technical staff: the Chief personally met suppliers and discussed such technicalities as bogies, forgings, steel specs. Unlike Churchward, Gresley regarded these external contracts as more important than internal technical advances..." (p47).

This approach must have been reinforced by Ivatt whilst Gresley was Carriage and Wagon Superintendent, and more particular during the transition period of Gresley's take over of the CME post, when Ivatt and Gresley worked in unison. For example, in 1928 the design and build of the first 10 4-6-0s for the eastern section was given to the North British Locomotive Company. Clearly Gresley was happy to help sell his suppliers' wares, no doubt seeing this as an aid to development by way of increased revenue, and a well-known photograph has a delegation from Romania, led by General Mihail Jonescu, Director-General of the Romanian State Railways on 9th November 1931, platform 11 Kings Cross. *Royal*

Forester formed a special to Hatfield. Gresley is featured and his close friend and boss, Sir Ralph Wedgewood (ex-NER incidentally) also appears, and is clearly of the same mind.

Sir Ralph had extolled the virtues of the Sentinels very publicly in other arenas. Beaumont (in his 1927 paper to the Institution of Locomotive Engineers) cited part of Sir Ralph Wedgewood's presidential address to the Railway Students Association in which he stated that: "experiments have been made in the use of autocar (push and pull trains) with petrol cars and with the Sentinel steam car which give promise of being much more successful. Experience with the latter car seems to indicate that we may look for considerable economics by the adoption of this unit".

The file referred to the requirement of an outline of a smaller Yarrow/Gresley boiler. I have found a drawing of K3 2-6-0 with water-tube boiler from July 1931, reviewed in 1932. Clearly this is a 2-6-0 version of 10000, including that striking front end, and there is a startling similarity with a product proposed by Sentinel in 1932. This has the boiler that was almost certainly the one proposed for the K3, but on a very different chassis. The K3 was "worked up" by the LNER under the instruction of Gresley. I wonder who gave Sentinel the instruction to work up the 1,600 B.H.P. Express Locomotive with the same boiler, albeit with considerably extended water drums. It is the same height, and has the distinctive cladding shape and front-end arrangements as the K3 and 10000. The conventional chassis has been replaced with compound steam motors, standard to the Sentinels, nose suspended on bogies, with a coal bunker and reserve tank. This machine would have had, without a shadow of doubt, nowhere near the appetite for coal and water of the K3 simple; this, combined with the extended water drums and reserve tank, eliminates the need for a tender. 3 tons of coal would give a considerable range between refills. I wonder how far this particular machine got?

Sentinel did build a class with Woolnough boilers, which are clearly a metre gauge version of the K3 development, but for Columbia. The boiler cladding is 100% Hush-Hush even down to the bright boiler bands. A well-known photograph of one of these machines was taken in 1934, in Belgium, under test. In front of the locomotive from left to right, H.N. Gresley, CBE, CME LNER; Julian S Tritton, Messrs Rendel, Palmer and Tritton, Consulting Engineers to Indian State Railways; S.E. Alley, Director, The Sentinel Wagon Works Ltd (and patent holder); J. Clayton, MBE, Personal Assistant to the CME, Southern Railway; W.A. Stanier, CME LMS; O. Bulleid, Assistant to

CME LNER; J.S. Robson, Messrs Robson and Smith, Brussels; Commander H.V. Gaud, Director, Sentinel Waggon Works Ltd; C. Jansens, Director, SNCF Columbie, Brussels; F.W. Hawksworth, Assistant to CME GWR; W.L. Watson, Deputy Chief Engineer, The Crown Agents for the Colonies; A.W. Smith, Messrs Robson and Smith Brussels; E. Hennig, Belgian National Railway Co; J Ortmans, Managing Director of l'Industrie Louvain and Director of SNCF Columbie; Mr Seressia, CME Vicuña Rly Co; Mr Dulieu, District Engineer, Vicinaux Rly Co.

Julian S Tritton, next to Gresley, was to write a paper for the Institution of Locomotive Engineers twelve years later, in which he noted that the locomotive had excellent ride and reached 56 mph. He was, in his paper, explaining the advantages of locomotives, such as Garratts, Mallets and other multi-cylinder designs, which had naturally evolved into the machine above, with all of the weight on driven wheels and adhesive.

Sentinel also had proposals for two-axle rigid 300hp, three-axle rigid 450hp and four-axle articulated, for which the Columbian was prototype. These were to have Woolnough boilers and compound or simple axle-hung steam motors. With these and products of other companies/railways, all classes of prime mover would be covered by steam locomotives of clean, modern, economic design.

The Sentinel boilers were reputed to last from seven to as many as ten years. It therefore seems that the railcars lasted through two cycles of boilers, one "as built" and one replacement. Almost all lasted fourteen to eighteen years, being introduced in significant numbers circa 1930 and withdrawn circa 1946. The Woolnoughs lasted only one cycle; in their case it was almost certainly because they went out of fashion. As for the Columbian, I don't know.

The Sentinel Volume 2 1930-1980 by Anthony R & Joseph L Thomas provides images and details.

This was not the end for the Sentinel design as Bulleid picked up the baton. He produced a spectacular Sentinel with Brotan/Bulleid boiler and Uniflow motors, the Leading Class. The Bulleid Merchant Navy Class had thermic siphons, water tubes of a kind, in a "conventional" boiler. These boilers lasted to the end of express passenger steam, and continue in preservation. Unfortunately there is no definitive evidence that I am aware of to support the reputed superiority of these boilers; however, in a last ditch attempt to secure a future for steam (and the planet?) Bulleid built *Leader* with a modified Brotan boiler incorporating thermic syphons and sleeve valves for the uniflow cylinders.

Note that Gresley had modified a Brotan, but removed the resemblance to a conventional boiler by replacing the barrel with drums and banks of tubes. Bulleid took a step backwards and retained the normal barrel but replaced the firebox wall tubes, normal for Brotans, with already tried and tested thermic siphons, four of them. The motors had chain-driven valve gear, and the final drive was a development of the ones used on the highly successful Sentinel locomotives. The sleeve valves had been successful in aircraft. All wheels were driven, some by chains in true Sentinel fashion. This was clearly the next step from the Columbian locomotives and the fruition of the LNER water tube K3. Popular history suggests that this was a failure. This cannot be true. André Chapelon congratulated Bulleid on his successful *Leader* having almost certainly, in some way, been involved in the development. Chapelon had said that the next development would be a modified Brotan. The regular driver of *Leader* seemed to be happy enough, I understand, in spite of the inevitable teething troubles with such experiments.

The Irish Railway went on to employ Bulleid, and he produced a "turf burning" version, which would never have been sanctioned if *Leader* had been a total failure. Sadly, the turf burner was cut up three years before 10000's water-tube boiler, in 1962.

In 1951 there was a drive to remove all non-standard locomotives from British Railways and the *Leaders* were withdrawn, some before they were completed. British Railways continued with the Midland/LMSR "make steam as easy to maintain as possible and forget development" policy that had been in vogue for many years. In the final outcome Gresley and William Stanier's testing station provided us with absolutely nothing of any long-term value.

Locomotive Test Facilities

In France, André Chapelon had access to a testing station with rolling road suitable for several thousand horsepower to test machines and drive development forward. In his Presidential address to the Institution of Locomotive Engineers, Gresley made a plea for a locomotive testing station.

"About six years ago the French engineers, who were fully alive to the benefits which would be derived by the provision of a testing station, were able to persuade the French Government that it was necessary to have such a station. Just over twelve months ago the French station at Vitry, near Paris, was opened, and the following day I [Gresley] had the privilege of seeing one of the largest express passenger engines undergoing tests at over 60 miles per hour on full load in the new station.

"This experimental station is the most perfectly equipped in the world for carrying out analytical and scientific research into the working of that most wonderful yet thermally inefficient machine – the railway locomotive. The station has been described in full detail in the technical press. It is of interest to note that the hydraulic brakes... absorb the whole of the power developed by the locomotive, and are of such substantial design that each is capable of absorbing 1,200 h.p. continuously for long periods. The plant is designed to test locomotives having an axle load up to 30 tons running at all speeds up to 100 m.p.h. Provision is made for six hydraulic brakes, so that locomotives having six driving axles and capable of exerting up to 7,200 h.p. can be tested.

"There are also four new dynamometer cars fitted with the most modern recording appliances... can also be used for checking the results of innovations which have been introduced as a result of research in the locomotive experimental station.

"The total cost incurred in the construction of the station was about £120,000, exclusive of the dynamometer cars.

"The French railways, since the establishment some years ago of the Office Centrale des Etudes de Material in Paris, have made such pronounced progress in the design and scientific development of their engines that today their modern locomotives are second to none... such as the provision of extra large steam passages and a double blast-pipe. There was no real novelty in these features, but the French engineers had worked out the designs scientifically and had proved them by the results obtained in actual service...

"What have we here in England? A small locomotive testing plant of 500 h.p. capacity, installed at the Swindon works of the Great Western Railway thirty years ago...The Swindon plant is, however, much too small for modern locomotives.

"There are four dynamometer cars in existence on British Railways, all of which I regard as almost obsolete when compared with modern cars.

"Before concluding my address, it is appropriate to refer to the tendency today towards the speeding up of all trains, and to make some reference to the extra high-speed passenger trains which have recently been introduced abroad...

"The question is naturally asked, why has nothing been done here beyond speeding up the existing steam-operated trains? The answer, of course, is the difficulty in finding on our congested railways a path for trains of such exceptional speeds. The permanent way of the British railways is well known to be the most perfect in the world, as is also the method of signalling, and there is no question that trains of the highest speed contemplated can be run with safety and comfort on our railways.

"It is not suggested that speeds much in excess of 100 m.p.h. can economically be maintained. The air resistance, notwithstanding scientific streamlining, absorbs so much power. Experiments with models of existing types of coaches carried out by the National Physical Laboratory show that the air resistance of trains of average length, say twelve coaches, at 100 m.p.h., is approximately double that of similar trains at 70 m.p.h. In the case of the 'Flying Hamburger,' in which I recently travelled, it is calculated that 85 per cent of the power generated by the Diesel engines is absorbed in air resistance when running at 100 m.p.h. Streamlining is essential at extra high speeds because air resistance of trains increases approximately as the cube of the speed, but it is of comparatively negligible value at lower speeds, up to, say, 50 m.p.h. I think that the day is not far distant when heavy trains consisting of one class only will be run at speeds not less than the best speeds of today, and that short extra high-speed trains, for which a supplement will be charged, will be run between London and the big industrial centres. The steam locomotive, however, of greatly improved efficiency, as a result of the establishment of a locomotive experimental station, will still continue as the chief power unit operating on our railways..."

From the *Journal of the Institution of Locomotive Engineers* No. 121 (September-October 1934)

The official photograph of the amazing 242.A.1. 5000 horses! (The French National Railway Museum)

Chapelon – The Results of Having Locomotive Test Facilities
SNCF 242.A.1

The cylinder arrangement of this locomotive had been tried on 10000 when it ran as a pseudo three cylinder. The system on 242.A.1 consists of one high-pressure cylinder in series with two low-pressure cylinders in parallel with each other at 135 degrees 90 degrees and 135 degrees, 90 degrees between the low-pressure. In effect, a single cylinder machine giving 5500 horsepower! 10000 tested this by using the two high-pressure cylinders sized to give half the power of each of the low. The vector sum of the two half power, high-pressure cylinders, was one high-pressure cylinder of the same power as one low-pressure. The angles of the cylinders were, starting at the low pressure; low pressure 90 degrees to next low pressure, in turn 135 degrees to the vector sum of the high pressure cylinders then 135 degrees to the starting point.

242.A.1, a rebuild, gave 5500 cylinder horsepower. This was a direct result of the ability to thoroughly test locomotives both in the laboratory, in strictly controlled conditions, as well as on the road.

In *La Locomotive a Vapeur (*translated by G.W. Carpenter), Chapelon states:

"It is characterised principally by the use of three-cylinder compound drive and by its boiler with greater evaporative power, including a combustion chamber and a fire grate of $5m^2$ … This locomotive was created by the rebuilding of the former ETAT three cylinder simple 4-8-2 No. 241.101 and left the works of the ACTIERS DE SAINT CHAMOND in the spring of 1946 … Very soon afterwards it commenced power output tests on service trains … Trains of 600 to 660 tons were hauled over the difficult line from Lyon to St Germain-des-Fosses via St. Etienne with very substantial gains on schedule."

(Gains on schedule can be achieved by established slack timings, but in this case it was wholly due to the nature of the beast.)

"For example, on June 20th 1946, 47 min. 20secs were regained on the Bordeaux – Geneva train between St Germain-des-Fosses and Lyon (206 km) with 16 coaches, 664 tons … Actual drawbar h.p. of between 3000 and 3500 was recorded frequently, corresponding to 3500 to 4000 db.h.p. on level track at constant speed … Even higher peak outputs were recorded … Contrary to a view sometimes held on three cylinder compound locomotives, 242.A.1 has never shown any unusual tendency to wheel slip. Restarting from Saint Chamond on an effective grade of 1.4% (1/71) was always without difficulty, and without banking assistance. Drawbar pulls of 25 tons (approx 55800 lbs) have been exerted at starting, which is equivalent to the maximum adhesion coefficient of one third which it is possible to achieve on dry rails"

From this, we can see the following:

Cut off: 75% high-pressure/50% low-pressure
Speed: 100 km/hr (67 mph)
Boiler pressure: 20atm (300psi)
Intermediate receiver: 10atm (150psi)

Power in high-pressure cylinder: 1870 horsepower

Power in low-pressure cylinders: 3530 horsepower

Ratio = 0.53 (0.5 would be ideal)
                    Total: 5400 horsepower

Each low-pressure cylinder 1765 horsepower compared with 1870 horsepower in the high-pressure.

Cut off: 60% high-pressure/50% low-pressure
Speed: 118 km/hr (79 mph)
Boiler pressure: 20atm (300psi)
Intermediate receiver: 9.5atm (140psi)

Power in high-pressure cylinder: 1920 horsepower

Power in low-pressure cylinders: 3580 horsepower

Ratio = 0.537 (0.5 would be ideal)
                    Total: 5500 horsepower

Each low-pressure cylinder 1790 horsepower compared with 1920 horsepower in the high-pressure.

Looking back to 1935, the final set of trial figures in the file indicates how 10000 was doing in comparison. A sample of cut offs were as follows (high pressure/low pressure):

30/25, 30/35, 30/45, 30/55, 40/25, 40/45, 40/55, and 50/25, 50/40, 50/45, 50/55.

No long cut offs in the high pressure cylinders! Gresley would have failed to get anywhere near utilising the capabilities of the boiler, although it has to be said that this was not his aim. He went to some

242.A.1 at Vitry: *What would Gresley have given for this facility? Is that André Chapelon casually discussing issues with an engineer in the front of 242.A.1 at full throw, standing still? What a moment to capture! (Thierry Stora)*

length to keep to the power of the contemporary Pacifics. Had it not been for *Silver Link* I am sure that the next machine would have been the one André Chapelon built, but with a 450psi boiler, and what a machine that would have been! With long high-pressure cut offs André Chapelon achieved these staggering horsepower figures with a 300psi boiler.

How Could This Be?

For 10000, the exhaust from the 10in high-pressure cylinders went to a receiver and, at some time during 1935, re-superheaters, before entering the low-pressure cylinder. (There were no documents regarding fitting of intermediate superheaters in the file but the temperatures for left and right are recorded on the test results of 1935.) However,

The total volume of the HP cylinders
$$= Pi \times 10 \times 10 \times 4L / 4$$
$$= 100PiL \text{ cubic inches}$$
The total volume of the LP cylinders
$$= Pi \times 20 \times 20 \times 4L / 4$$
$$= 400PiL \text{ cubic inches}$$

The volume of the set for work done during the cycle is the total of these = 500PiL cubic inches

Note that we are talking about swept volume here, not length of stroke, and that the system is not four individual cylinders but two high-pressure in parallel, in series with two low-pressure in parallel. High pressure followed on by low pressure.

Let us consider the range of cut offs for a simple expansion cylinder equivalent, say 20%, 40%, 60% and 80%, which are very approximately the kind of numbers utilised for expansive working for various conditions: 80% for starting, 20% for cruising.

Now, if we replace these simple cylinders by the compound cylinders above, but use the simple cut off equivalents, we get:

- 20% of 500PiL gives 100PiL, the full stroke of the HP followed on at 0% in the LP

- 40% of 500PiL gives 200PiL, the full stroke of the HP followed on at 25% in the LP

- 60% of 500PiL gives 300PiL, the full stroke of the HP followed on at 50% in the LP

- 80% of 500PiL gives 400PiL, the full stroke of the HP followed on at 75% in the LP

All practical constraints apart, this is why we need long cut offs in the high-pressure cylinders. If the high-pressure cylinder is cut off early, it will perform no better than a simple! It will be, in effect, strangled. Chapelon continues:

"During tests with 242A.1 at Vitry testing station and on the road using brake locomotives excellent results have been obtained, both in terms of coal and water consumption and in power output. For the first time in Europe 4000h.p. was sustained at the tender drawbar on a continuous basis (with constant pressure and water level) this being equivalent to 800h.p. per m^2 of grate area and to an output of more than 5000 cylinder h.p. and this at speeds of 80 km/hr. (with 80% H.P. and 50% L.P. cut off) and at 100 km/hr. (with 70% H.P. and 45% L.P.) At 120 km/hr. 3800 drawbar h.p. was sustained, using 60% H.P. and 40% L.P. cut off.

"Notable though they are, these results, for a locomotive working at 20atm. with 400 deg steam temperature, with a grate area no larger than 5 m^2 and only 21 t. coupled axle loading, are far from exhausting the possibilities still open to the locomotive designer and builder, even independently from further progress in the thermal and thermodynamic fields which can now be envisaged.

"This makes abundantly clear the enormous potential still available within the very simple concept of the classic steam locomotive which, 120 years after being fashioned by the genius of Stephenson, Hackworth and Seguin, thus shows itself still capable of competing with all other forms of prime mover, even the most recent".

This was written over half a century ago by André Chapelon. Notice that Hackworth is up there alongside Stephenson (which one?) and Seguin. Gresley talked of 70% HP cut offs before he was persuaded otherwise. The machine that Chapelon produced here was in Gresley's head twenty years earlier!

What Were the Developments That Chapelon Had in Mind?

La Locomotive a Vapeur states:

"In his paper to the Ingenieurs Civils de France in 1949, reviewing steam locomotive development and future possibilities, André Chapelon suggested that the next logical step would be to use much higher boiler pressures with triple expansion drive to reduce the specific water consumption of a locomotive of similar basic dimensions to three-cylinder compound 4-8-4 No. 242.A.1 from 6.5 kg/db h.p. /hr to 4.75 kg. With a corresponding increase in sustained cylinder indicated power from 5000 to 7000, equivalent to 21.5 kg of locomotive weight per i.h.p., a figure never previously achieved.

"This would require the use of a tubular boiler barrel with water tube firebox of modified Brotan type, as used on Baldwin prototype 4-10-2 No. 60,000 and further developed by Lawford Fry of the steam locomotive research institute to work at 40atm. (600psi) with resuperheat, steam jacketing and possibly a modification to the phases of steam distribution"

The steam to the HP cylinder was direct from the 600psi boiler, but the cylinders were to be steam jacketed to stop the wall effect. The exhaust from this was to a superheater before the intermediate-pressure cylinder. This cylinder has superheated steam and the jacket is not needed. Finally the exhaust from this is superheated again before use in the two low-pressure cylinders, again no jacket needed.

Of course Chapelon had more in mind than just sloggers. The projected high-speed steam locomotive was capable of 167mph, not forgetting that Chapelon could predict to within 3% of actual.

Chapelon continues:

"Subsequently studies were made of the potential for increased power output in large American locomotives by the use of compound and triple expansion drive, combined with resuperheat, steam jacketing, enlarged steam circuits and more efficient draughting arrangements. In the case of a locomotive of similar basic dimensions to the Union Pacific "Big Boy" type

4-8-8-4, André Chapelon estimated that, extrapolating from results with 4-8-4 No. 242.A.1, with compound drive using two H.P. cylinders on the rigid frame unit, and three L.P. on the leading truck unit, pressure of 22atm. (330psi) and boiler barrel preheater as in 160.A.1 [and the LNWR 2-2-2-2], maximum drawbar power could be increased to 12,000 h.p. Continuously. But with a water tube firebox boiler working at 40atm. (600psi) and triple expansion drive with steam jacketed H.P. cylinder, superheat to the I.P. cylinders and resuperheat to the L.P. (one H.P. and two I.P. on the rigid frame and three L.P. on the leading truck unit) a further increase of 33% in power would be possible, thus raising maximum output to the order of 16,000 drawbar h.p."

In André Chapelon's words:

"Such power outputs would be of great value at higher speeds and would be achieved by a single locomotive unit, without involving the costly fixed installations of electric traction or the multiplicity of diesel engines of limited power with diesel traction. They bring into sharp focus the extraordinary unexploited potential of the steam locomotive, which for more than a century, has never failed to meet the ever increasing demands of a modern and rapidly expanding world economy."

Marc de Caso

Marc de Caso produced Baltic, four-cylinder compound locomotives with rotary cam valve gear. The valve gear was later changed for Walschaerts driving oscillating cam poppet valves. The three-cylinder simple with rotary cam valve gear built for comparative trials, looked the same, but in regular service the simples burned 14% more coal. It is reported that the de Caso locomotives were not as good as Chapelon's.

A little fuzzy now, as is the author's memory of standing on the front of Big Boy in 1985, but little did I know that this machine would feature in a book about 10000 and that it would be left to me to reveal the W1 story straight from that amazing archive. (Author's Collection)

One of the Union Pacific Railroad's twenty-five 4000 class 4-8-8-4 articulated steam locomotives built between 1941 and 1944 by Alco. No 4004 is preserved at Holliday Park, Cheyenne, Wyoming, and is seen here on 17th May 2010. (Mike Pannell)

The Rebuild and the Final Years

Boilers at the beginning of the 21st Century

Sentinel Sized Steam Generator of the 21st Century

The steam generator's heaters are made with coils made of seamless tubes, where the feed water is preheated and evaporated during the flow through these. The heat is transferred to the water/steam mixture as radiant heat in the combustion chamber, where the inner cylindrical tube coil and a flat tube coil form the chamber wall and the bottom respectively. Consequently, refractory concrete is avoided. The combustion gasses are hereafter cooled in the outer convection part, as the gasses pass the space between the two tube coils. The thermal design ensures a modest volume of steam relative to the size of the heater, and allows unlimited thermal expansion due to the high temperatures. All TT boilers steam generators and steam boilers are designed and equipped according to German TRD boiler regulations and Danish boiler regulations and corresponding EN-norms.

High Efficiency Boiler/Turbine in the 21st Century

The Mitsui Babcock two-pass advanced supercritical (ASC) boiler is described as follows:

"The furnace walls from the hopper inlet to the furnace arch nose level are of vertical tube membrane wall construction. The low mass flux technology inherently ensures a positive flow characteristic, which means the tubes with higher than average heat pick-up have a higher than average water flow without the need for adjustable orifices or similar means to control temperature. An optimised profile of the internal ribs of the low mass flux vertical furnace tubes is essential.

"The main advantages identified are:
- Lower capital costs:
  - Self-supporting tubes, hence simplifying part of the boiler support system
  - Elimination of transition headers at spiral/ vertical interface
  - Simpler ash hopper tubing geometry.
- Lower operating costs:
  - Lower overall boiler pressure drop, hence lower auxiliary power load resulting in higher plant output and higher efficiency
  - 'Positive flow characteristic' automatically compensates for variations in furnace absorptions compared to the negative flow characteristics of the spiral furnace
- Simple and economic tube repair
- Simple start-up system; a start-up circulation pump is not required
- Reduced slagging of furnace walls

Lower part loads down to 20% are possible while maintaining high steam temperatures."

(From *Advanced Power Plant Using High Efficiency Boiler/Turbine*, DTI, Best Practice Brochure, Carbon Abatement Technologies Programme, BPB010 January 2006, DTI Pub URN 06/665.)

Pressure Temperature Specifications of the Latest Boilers

bar	psi	c	f
241	3615	538	1000.4
241	3615	538	1000.4
247	3705	571	1059.8
259	3885	569	1056.2
266	3990	600	1112
250	3750	600	1112
275	4125	580	1076
262	3930	545	1013
244	3660	540	1004
260	3900	540	1004
290	4350	582	1079.6
285	4275	580	1076
300	4500	580	1076

Exploration of the properties of steam over the range 15psi to 4500psi, dry saturated up to 3200psi and using the pressures and temperatures quoted for the latest supercritical boilers, reveals some interesting discoveries, but one chart in particular is of note. Using the imperial system, to keep in context with Gresley's days, I have produced "Variation of Btu/lb (H) with Pressure (P)" the graph of which is reproduced on the next page. It is either remarkable, or Gresley knew exactly what he was doing: the fact is that the amount of heat per pound of steam is at a maximum at 450psi when dealing with sub-critical steam. To improve on this the pressure needs to go to a supercritical 3500psi and about 1000 degrees F.

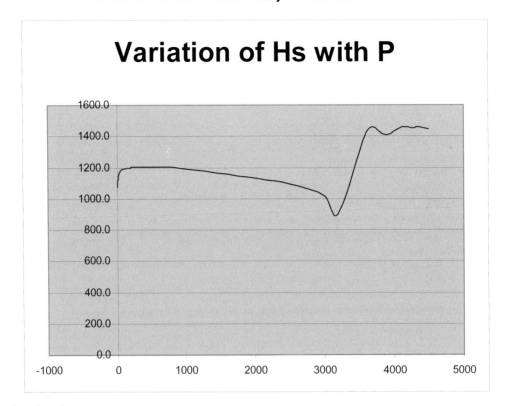

Variation of Btu/lb with Pressure

It is also of particular note that the DTI brochure uses the words that Gresley used three-quarters of a century ago. "The law of diminishing returns applies". In other words, now, at a supercritical 4500psi we appear to have reached another peak in heat per pound of steam. One limiting factor is in the capabilities of the metals economically available that will withstand the conditions, including high temperatures.

No doubt you will look at this graph and say that it doesn't make sense but here is something from the World Wide Web that says it all:

"Thermodynamics is a funny subject
At first you understand it, except for one or two points
Then you realise you don't understand it at all
But by now you are used to it
So it doesn't matter."

Summary

It is no wonder that this book has taken so long to come to fruition. Almost all of the Hush-Hush works, that I have read, failed to tell the story, using the stock statement "it had technical difficulties". Some tried better but still missed the essence. I am sure that some commentators have seen "The File" and have used a very small, *ad hoc*, fraction of the material, but missed crucial points. Having read the file myself, it soon became obvious that in order to understand 10000, some background, which may go beyond the casual reader's knowledge, is essential. I therefore began by looking at the "Search for Efficiency", providing an elementary view of the synthesis needed to get to the LNER extra-high-pressure compound Pacific, finally to become Baltic. This takes us on a journey into the past and across the Northern Hemisphere. Beyond this I had to decide how much of "The File" to give to the reader, and the most efficient way of doing it. I have summarised my findings along with the appropriate images kindly provided by the Ken Hoole Collection Executors and North Road Museum who were glad to see me finish off a work that he had started by producing an album. The epilogue brings us back to the present with the developments post "10000 water tube and compound", including the fascinating evolution to Leader, through Sentinel, and finally where the technology is today.

Appendix A

List of Drawings

19-Apr-26	Yarrow	On A1 Frame
19-May-26	Yarrow	On A1 Frame
19-Oct-28	LNER	4-6-4 Diagram
18-Feb-28	12613	Frame Arrangement
1928	12614	Relative Position of Tyre
	12620	Position of Reducing Valve on Steam Drum
	12654	LP Cylinders
	12659	HP Piston and Hollow Rod
	12660	HP Front Cylinder Cover
	12677	Proposed Smokebox and Assembly of Front End
	12697	Assembly of Frames at Back End
	12698	LP Piston and Hollow Rod
	12701	Built Up Crank Axle
	12708	LP Front Cylinder Cover
	12725	HP & LP Cylinder Steam Pipes
	12733	Straight Axle
	12734	Axle for Bissel Truck and Bogies
	12737	3' - 2" Trailing Wheel Axle
	12740	Outline of Piston Stuffing Box LP Cylinder
	12742	Hornblock Intermediate
	12743	Hornblock Leading & Trailing
	12752	Outline of Piston Stuffing Box HP Cylinder
	12754	Back Piston Valve Cover Gland & Packing HP Cyl
	12768	Back Piston Valve Cover Gland & Packing LP Cyl
	12778	Carrying Wheel Hornblocks
	12785	Proposed Assy of Regulating Valves Reversing Shaft Ashpan
	12787	Valve Motion Table
	12789	Piston Valve, Liner & Spindle
	12800	Axle Box for Carrying Wheels
	12803	Wedges, Hornguides Oilbox for Carrying Wheel Axleboxes
	12807	LP Piston Valve, Liner and Spindle
	12810	Leading and Trailing Coupling Rods
	12811	Inside Connecting Rod & Strap
	12812	Outside Connecting Rod
	12817	Bogie Wheel 2' - 8"
	12818	Cast Steel Frame Stay
	12822	Support for Guide Shoes for Boiler Feet and Back Water Drum
	12823	Frame Stay Support for Guide Shoes for Boiler Feet on Front End of Front Water Drum
	12825	Support for 11" dia Steam Brake Cylinder
	12826	Liner for HP Cylinder
	12828	LP Front Piston Valve Cover
	12829	Frame Stay & Support for Guide Shoes for Boiler on Back and of Front Water Drum
	12832	Front Corner Stays Between Inner and Main Frames
	12833	LP Front Piston Valve Cover
	12834	Stay Between Inner and Main Frames
	12842	Stay Between Inner and Main Frames
	12850	Support for Reversing Shaft & Lifting Link Brackets
	12855	Cast Steel Dragbox & Frame Stays
	12859	Motion Bars HP
	12860	Motion Bars LP
	12865	Axlebox Guides
	12873	Leading Driving Wheels

1928 cont.	12874	Intermediate Driving Wheels
	12875	Trailing Driving Wheels
	12878	Arrangement of Bissel Truck
	12885	Bogie & Bissel Truck Wheels
	12886	Carrying Wheels
	12900	Bissel Truck Main Casting
	12917	Front Boiler Support
	12931	Crosshead
	12937	Details of Bissel Truck
	12938	?
	12945	Bogie Control Castings
	12954	Bogie Frame Template
	12960	Combined Rocking Shaft & HP Expansion Link
	12964	Spring Stops (Bogie)
	12972	Spring Hanger Brackets
	12975	Proposed Modification to Air Casing & Smokebox
	12980	Bogie Bearing Spring
	12982	Blast Pipe Blower Ring
	12989	Combined Frame Stay & Radius Bar Pivot
	12990	Bearing Spring for Bissel Truck
	12995	Bogie Details
	13000	Leading Driving Axleboxes
	13010	Bissel Truck & Radius Bar Details
	13014	Intermediate & Trailing Driving Axleboxes
	13029	Various Bore "Robey" Type Valve Ross Patent
	13030	Various Bore "Robey" Type Valve Ross Patent
	13031	Various Bore "Robey" Type Valve Ross Patent
	13032	Details of Engine Draw Gear
	13035	Metcalf's Patent Vacuum Ejector
	13037	Carrying Spring
	13041	Steam Manifold in Cab (Diagram)
	13044	Reversing Shaft
	13046	Spring Stops for Carrying Wheels
	13051	Brackets for Reversing Shaft
	13059	Leading Sandboxes
1929	13061	HP Reversing Shaft
	13062	Spring for Carrying wheel
	13063	No 9 Injector HP D&M
	13064	No 11 Injector GA fig 2 Hot water pattern G&C
	13071	LP Expansion Link
	13076	Driving Sand Boxes
	13080	Arrangement of Bogie
	13085	Lubricator for Axle Box Tray
	13088	H&S patent Compound Spring for Bissel Truck
	13098	Valve Spindle Crosshead
	13100	Footplate Details
	13101	Fallplate on Smokebox Saddle Casting
	13105	Motion Arrangement
	13106	Sand Ejector
	13110	Smokebox Front Plate
	13112	Diagram Showing Relative Positions of Balance Weights
	13119	Bracket for Steam Reversing Gear Cylinders
	13127	Steam Cylinder for Steam Reversing Gear
	13128	Oil Cylinder

List of Drawings

1929 cont.	13636	Retaining Ring for Piston Rod Packing
	13646	Whistle & Details
	13652	Position of Vacuum Ejector Pipe
	13653	Chimney
	13655	Pipe & Rod Arrangement
	13657	Arrangement of Vacuum Ejector Pipe
	13662	Blower Valve
	13665	?
	13667	Whistle & Details
	13670	Proposed Telemotor Transmitter
	13672	T Piece for Mechanical Lubricator
	13680	Steam Brake Valve Bracket
	13697	Bracket for Telemotor Receiver
	13700	Alteration to Class S Tender footplate to suit 4-6-4HP
	13703	Lever for Receiver Supplied by Mactaggart
	13704	T piece for Steam Sanding Gear
	13705	Bracket for Telemotor Receiver HP Reversing Gear
	13706	Steam Chest Pressure Gauge Cocks
	13707	Relative Position of Axle Box Tops & Engine Frame in Running Position
	13708	Bracket for Telemotor Receiver
	13711	Footplate Steps
	13712	Feedwater connections for HP & LP Injectors
	13720	Safety Spring & Sleeve
	13725	Tender Axle
	13729	Front Cylinder Cover for Outside Cylinder
	13738	Cylinder Drain Cocks
	13741	Relative Position of Engine North British Loading Gauge & Distributive Weights
	13746	Driver's Seat
	13761	Bracket for Motion Bar Oil Boxes
	13762	Wood Platform, Fall Plate & Door between Engine & Tender
	13767	Detail of Cab Roof Showing A1 Cut at Lifting Doors
	13768	Cover for Hole in Tender Top Plate
	13770	Support for Gauges & Telemotor Replenishing Tank
	13774	Levers & Brackets for Regulator Controls
	13778	Nameplates
	13796	Detail of Cast Steel Support for Superheater Element
	13800	Fog Signal Arrangement & Details
	13804	Element Support
	13809	Details of Pyrometer
	13810	Cut off Lubricating Gear Details
	13811	Handrail Pillars and Head Lamp Bracket
	13812	Splasher for Leading Driving Wheels
	13813	Brick Arch
	13814	Nameplate for Manifold
	13815	Access Doors In Casing
	13818	Boiler Drain Valve
	13819	Registration Number Plate
	13820	Transmittors for Cut off Indicator
	13822	Mild Steel Details for Cut Off Indicating Gear
	13823	Receivers for Cut off Indication
	13825	Arrangement of Transmitter & Rods for Indication
	13833	Alteration to Injector Valves
	13840	Alteration to Drain Valve
1930	13844	Arrangement & Deatails of Handrails & Pillars 5000 Gal Corridor Tender
	13845	Rod & Stuffing Box for Drain Valve

List of Drawings

1930 cont.	14281	Position of holes in Frames for Operating Blowdown Valves of Front Ware Drums
	14282	Method of Operating Blow Down Valves on Back Water Drums
	14293	Details of Blower in Centre Flue
	14295	Superheater Assembly
	14296	Details of Superheater
	14297	Details of Superheater
	14298	Details of Superheater
	14299	Details of Superheater
	14300	Details of Superheater
	14301	Details of Superheater
	14344	Firedoor & Details
1931	14366	Assembly of Extensive Spring Fitted to 3" Throttle Valve
	14373	Reservoir for Telemotor for HP & LP Reversing Gear
	14397	Water Gauge Fittings
	14492	Arrangement of Steam & Water Drums Arch Tubes
	14493	Detail of Steam Drum
	14506	Independent Feed Steam to HP Injector
	14507	Hole in Frame to Facilitating Oiling Bissel Truck
	14522	Lagging Mats for Drum Ends
	14553	Stop Valve for Steam Supply to HP Injector
	14629	Blast Pipe & Blower Ring
	14630	Adaptor for Soot Filter for CO_2 Recorder
	14635	Bronze Unions for Indicating Gear
	14639	Details for Indicating Gear
	14640	Arrangement of Indicating Gear
	14647	Assembly and Details for Air Pipe in Ashpan
	14649	Detail of Container for Feed Water from Weir
	14650	Temperature of Water in Weir (assy & details)
	14663	Tank for Sodium Aluminate Water Softener
	14666	Arrangement of Proposed Modified Reducing Valve
	14696	No 10 Injector Class P
	14698	Guide for Drop Grate Operating Rod
	14712	Air Holes in Brick Arch Plate
	14713	Sketch Showing Steel Tube Pressed Into Position
	14715	1" Throttle Valve
	14732	Arrangement of Proposed Modified Reducing Valve
	14762	Boiler Drain Cock (Klinger)
	14779	Triplex Glass for Front Cab Windows (ordering print)
	14784	?
	14804	Arrangement of Proposed Modified Reducing Valve
1932	14835	Lever for LP Regulator
	14839	Boiler Drain Cocks on Front Water Drum
	14867	Hinged Firehole Door
	14870	HP Injector Steam Valves
	14872	Smoketube Proposed
	14934	Protection Plates Between Frames for HP Cylinders
	14943	Full Size Model Side Flue
	14959	Temporary Repair to Smokebox (left hand side)
	14979	Branch Piece for Smokebox
	14995	Firedoor Protector Plates
	15006	Arrangement of Superheater
	15007	Superheater Elements Spectacle Supporting Plates
	15008	Superheater Elements Spectacle Supporting Plates
	15012	Smoke Tube End

List of Drawings

1933 cont.	15400	Cylinder Water Cock Drain Details
	15402	Arrangement of Circulating Pipes
	15409	Arrangement of Cylinder Water Cock Gear
	15422	Detail of Vacuum Ejector Bracket
	15424	Standard Pipe Flanges for Pressures up to 450lbs
	15428	Arrangement & Details of Supports for operating rods for Hand Reversing Gear
	15434	Brackets, Steam Pipe Flange & Unions for Steam Brake Valve
	15454	Arrangement of Intermediate Superheater Inside Frames
	15457	Details of Headers for Back Water Drums
	15458	Detail of Back Water Drums
	15459	Detail of Front Water Drums
	15460	Arrangement of Steam & Water Drums
	15464	Details of Boiler Casings
	15465	Arrangement & Details of Duplex Cut Off Indicator
	15467	Arrangement of Ashpan & Drop Grate
	15468	Ashpan Mounting Arrangement Details
	15472	Baffle Plate for Superheater
	15473	Proposed Superheater between HP & LP Cylinders
	15488	Arrangement of Pipes Between Smokebox & Cylinders for Intermediate Superheater
	15503	Universal Joint for Operating Rods (Hand Reverse)(Companion Flanges)
	15542	Proposed Arrangement of Intermediate Superheater Supports
	15544	Arrangement of Aitons Pipes Between Cylinders & Smokebox
	15545	Circulating Pipes for Intermediate Superheater
	15547	Mild Steel Supports for Intermediate Superheater
	15548	Cast Steel Supports & Guides for Intermediate Superheater
	15553	Cover Plate & Cast Iron Cover for Steam Pipes
1934	15562	Details for Drain for Intermediate Superheater
	15564	5" Bore Cast Steel Pipe for Intermediate Superheater
	15566	Support for 5" Bore Pipes in Smokebox Intermediate Superheater
	15567	Cdlothing for Steam Pipes Intermediate Superheater
	15572	Arrangement Details of Feed Check Valves & Water Heater
	15574	Assembly of Intermediate Superheater Headers
	15575	Detail of Intermediate Superheater Headers
	15800	Yarrow Gresley Water Tube Boiler for LNER Outer Casing (Outside View)
	15801	Yarrow Gresley Water Tube Boiler for LNER Boiler Outer Casing (Sections)
	15802	Yarrow Gresley Water Tube Boiler for LNER Boiler Outer Casing (Framing Arrang't)
	15803	Boiler Outer Casing Details
	15840	Bearing Spring Details
	16009	No 8 -10 Injector Type HP (Left Hand)
	16010	No 8 -10 Injector Type HP (Right Hand)
1935	16065	Cowls for Chimney
	16072	Double Blast Pipe
	16082	Double Chimney
	16085	Setting Piece for Cowls (Double Chimney)
	16096	Arrangement of Double Blastpipe & Chimney
	16098	Cover for Double Chimney
	16100	Blower Ring & Tee Piece
	16122	Firebars
	16125	Arrangement of Firebars
	16285	Re-arrangement of Mountings in Cab
02-Jan-36	16431	Arrgt showing P2 boiler fitted to engine No 10000
	16820	Layout of Testing Plant Sheet 1 (1945)
	16821	Layout of Testing Plant Sheet 2 (1945)

The cast, in order of appearance

Name	Organisation	Position	Comments
A C Stamer	LNER	Chief Assistant Mechanical Engineer	
Herbert Nigel Gresley, later Sir Nigel Gresley	LNER	Chief Mechanical Engineer	
Mr Robson	LNER	Chief Draughtsman Darlington	
W E Dalby	C&G (Engineering) College		
R E Trevithick	Dewrance & Co Ltd		Water level indicators
Col. H A Stemming	The Superheater Company	Managing Director	Superheater
S Symes	LMSR	Works Manager	2 LNER 4-4-0 Compounds
Mr Marriner	Yarrow (Y&C)		
Alex L Mellor	Yarrow		
Mr L Horwill	Yarrow		
Mr MacNichol	Cockburns Ltd		Safety, reducing and regulator valves
	Davies & Metcalfe		Injector? and vacuum brake injector, low-pressure injector re 301229
Mr Pattinson	Darlington Forge	Chief Draughtsman	Also other castings and cylinder castings high-pressure steel re 301229
Mr Swift	Darlington Forge	Foundry Manager	
Mr Coupe	Darlington Forge	Foreman Patternmaker	
Mr Stephenson	LNER	Foreman Patternmaker	
Sir Thomas Putman	Darlington Forge	Managing Director	
D K Hamilton	Cockburns Ltd	Secretary	Safety, reducing and regulator valves
Mr Wm Reavell	Reavell & Co Ltd		Cylinder and steam chest liners cast iron
	Rivet Bolt And Nut Co Ltd		Boiler rivets
O.V.S. Bulleid	LNER		
Mr Heywood	LNER	Cowlairs	Yarrow wooden model showing air intake
Mr Gray	LNER	Assistant to Mr Robson?	
F W Carr	LNER	Loco Works Manager Darlington	
Richard S Metcalfe	Davies & Metcalfe	Director	
Harold Edgar Yarrow	Yarrow		
John T Wright	MacTaggart Scott & Co Ltd		Reverser telemotor
J Hogg	Yarrow		Ref to regulator handle
R A Thom	LNER	Doncaster	K3 1929 build reversing gear
Mr Lamb	MacTaggart Scott & Co Ltd	Fitter	
H H MacTaggart	MacTaggart Scott & Co Ltd	Director	
Mr Fraser	LMSR?		Movement of loco over LMS metals
	Hadfields of Sheffield		ERA IIR steel superheater tube support material re 301229 motion bar forgings
	A&W Dalglish		Firebars
	Messrs Brunton		MacTaggart Scott & Co Ltd
Mr J H Smeddle	LNER		Movement of new tender from Doncaster
Shed Foreman	LNER	York	Movement of new tender from Doncaster
Mr Neville Gresham, J N Gresham	Gresham & Craven		Injector cones and high-pressure injector and feedwater heaters re 301229
W A Faux	Gresham & Craven		Mr Gresham ill
R D Metcalfe	Davies & Metcalfe		
	J Blakeborough & Sons		Cocks and later piston valves, injector steam feed valves re 301229
	Beck & Co		Cocks
J W Mosley	J Blakeborough & Sons	Manager Steam Department	Piston valves

List of suppliers of parts for boiler and full specification, 18th December 1929		
Company	**Part**	**Order date**
J Brown & Co Ltd	Forged steel drums	5th March 1928
Chas McNeil Ltd	Steam water drum ends Manhole doors and dogs	12th March 1928 10th December 1928
Tubes Ltd	2in boiler tubes	8th May 1928
Weldless Steel Company	2½in O/D tubes Cold drawn steel pipes	8th May 1928 14th May 1929
Barr Thomson & Co	M S headers	12th June 1928
Steel Co	Steel plates & bars	4th March 1929
Glenboig Union Fireclay Co	Firebricks Special firebricks	7th May 1929 11th and 16th September 1929
D Harvey & Co Ltd	Copper pipes	11th May 1929
Castlecary Fireclay Co	Firebricks	7th September and 1st October 1929
Stewarts & Lloyds	Hot drawn tubes	26th September 1929
Carrick & Craig	Hot drawn tubes	26th September 1929

General list of suppliers, 30th December 1929	
Company	**Part**
Edgar Allen & Co	Bogie & Bissel Centres
Coltness Iron Works	Frame stays and other steel castings
T Summerson & Sons	Other steel castings
Steel Co of Scotland	Frame plates and straight axles
Monk Bridge Iron and Steel Company	Built up crank parts for assembling
Steel, Peech & Tozer	Tyres and laminated bearing springs
Wakefields Ltd	Mechanical lubricators and anti-carbonisers
Thos Firth & Sons Sheffield	Nickel chrome forgings for rods and combined pistons and rods – forgings
Kitson & Co Ltd	Cylinder castings low pressure cast iron
British Piston Ring Co	Piston and valve rings
British Metallic Packing Co	Piston rod packing rings
Manganese Bronze & Brass Co	Manganese bronze manifold
Aiton & Co	High and low pressure steam pipes and jointing rings
Skefko Ball Bearings Co	Ball bearings for radius rod

The cast, in order of appearance

Other people and organizations involved in the project

Name	Organisation	Position	Comments
P R Gresham	Gresham & Craven		Ejector prints
	Siemens Brothers & Co Ltd		Electrical indicator for valve gear position
	Chief Electrical Engineer		Electrical indicator for valve gear position
Mr Stedman	LNER Locomotive Running Department York		Boiler inspection
N H Scarth	LNER		Boiler inspection
Eric A Robinson	The Superheater Company	Manager Locomotive Department	Superheater
	J Stone & Co Ltd		Electric headlight system
W Massey	LNER CME Office		Photograph
R M D Thrupp	LNER CME Office		Photograph
A E Rogerson	LNER CME Office		Photograph
T Ferguson	LNER Stooperdale		Boiler inspection
Inspector Lowther	LNER Stooperdale	Boiler Inspector	Boiler inspection
Mr Needham	Evershed & Vignoles Ltd		With respect to indicator
Mr Copperthwaite	LNER Locomotive Running Department York		Run 30th January 1930
Driver Eltringham	LNER		Run 30th January 1930
Driver's Mate	LNER		Run 30th January 1930
Mr T Robson	LNER Chief Test Inspector		Run 30th January 1930
C M Jenkin Jones	LNER Superintendant		Run 6th February 1930
Mr J Davison	Programme office		Run 6th February 1930
C W L Glaze	LNER CME Dept Stratford		Duplex cut-off indicator
Mr A McDermid	Chief Draughtsman Stratford		Duplex cut-off indicator
	J Blakeborough & Sons		Sleeve valves
Mr Scarth	Yarrow		
Mr W Dryman	Cockburns Ltd		
	LNER	Advertising Sales Manager	Photographs
	Van Cytenbeek Sales Company		Paperweight
E Thompson	LNER Stratford		LP indicator rod
B Spencer Esq	LNER	CME Office	Photograph
MR CARR	LNER	Locomotive Running Superintendent York	
Driver Pennington			Exhibition KX and indicator test 18th May 1930
Fireman Slinger			Exhibition KX and indicator test 18th May 1930
	Yarrow		Mud door
S Johnston	Cockburns Ltd		
Mr Schlegel	LNER	Shed Superintendent Gateshead	Reducing valve drawing
W J Bamard	Bassett-Lowke Ltd		1in—1ft Model for American Museum of Science and Industry

Other people and organizations involved in the project, continued.

Name	Organisation	Position	Comments
Mr Clear	The Superheater Company		Tube sample
	Yarrow		Blakeborough blow down valves
P A Hyde	P A Hyde		Marcotty firedoor Thrupp
W Stewart	The Superheater Company		
S Marper	LNER		Memo from CME re papers
Mr Oxtoby	LNER		Memo from CME re papers
J H Gresham	Gresham & Craven		Confined to bed December 1930
The Secretary	Institution of Mechanical Engineers		
Driver J Gascoigne	LNER		Run of 20th January 1931 Darlington — Newcastle
Inspector Swan	LNER		
Mr C Dandrige	LNER	Advertising Manager	Advertising Poster 2nd June 1931
	Kersley & Co		Paint spec
J Simpson	LNER		Weights
	LNER	The Works Manager Gateshead	
Mr R S Turnbull	J Hopkinson & Co Ltd		Steam valves for high pressure working
Mr Baty	J Blakeborough & Sons		
	Smail, Sons & Co Ltd		Klinger valves not required
J C Metcalf	Davies & Metcalfe		
	Reed And Foggin Ltd		MacTaggart Scott & Co Ltd
A W D Tait	MacTaggart Scott & Co Ltd		
Mr Lamb	MacTaggart Scott & Co Ltd	Chief Draughtsman	
Mr Dick	LNER Shed Gateshead	Inspector	
H Spencer	LNER Darlington		Issuing Drawings
Driver T Turner	LNER Shed Gateshead		Satisfactory run 1st September 1932 Accompanied by H Spencer
Fireman J Bambra	LNER Shed Gateshead		Satisfactory run 1st September 1932 Accompanied by H Spencer
River G Horton	LNER Shed Gateshead		Run 8th September 1932 with RJR
	Benton & Stone Ltd		Examples of couplings
	Britains Ltd		Paperweight
L Farr	LNER	Works Manager by 17th August 1933	
	LNER	Mechanical Engineer Doncaster	2001 Mods for 10000
DG	LNER	CME Darlington Office	

Blast pipe tests

Date	HP cut off	LP cut off	Boiler	HP steam chest	LF receiver	Exhaust	Smokebox Vacuum	Smokebox temp	HP Super-heater temp	Receiver temp	LP Super-heater RH temp	LP Super-heater LH temp	Exhaust temp	Speed	Pull	Drawbar
D.M.Y	%	%	Psi No 1 bars	Psi	Ps.	Psi	Inches	Deg F	Deg F	Deg F	Deg F	Deg F	Deg F	mph	tons	Hp
30.5.35	30	25	450	415	120	1.00	1.00	510	635	-	597	435	244	55.0	-	-
30.5.35	30	25	460	420	120	0.75	1.00	505	595	-	495	440	222	57.5	-	-
30.5.35	30	35	440	400	80	1.00	1.50	530	600	-	465	418	223	60.0	-	-
30.5.35	30	35	470	425	85	1.00	1.50	550	640	-	477	435	223	59.5	0.63	225
30.5.35	30	35	435	395	84	1.00	1.50	545	635	-	488	438	217	57.5	0.63	218
30.5.35	30	35	430	395	80	0.75	1.50	525	625	-	482	435	216	54.7	0.48	147
30.5.35	30	45	445	400	60	1.25	2.25	535	625	-	475	425	234	61.0	0.78	285
30.5.35	30	45	430	390	60	1.25	2.50	550	640	-	480	428	237	58.0	0.87	300
30.5.35	30	45	465	415	70	1.50	2.75	545	650	-	477	428	235	60.5	0.91	330
30.5.35	30	45	470	420	65	1.00	2.50	555	640	-	474	428	235	61.5	0.86	315
30.5.35	30	45	450	400	60	1.00	2.50	560	645	-	479	425	232	62.5	0.80	300
30.5.35	40	25	455	410	165	1.00	1.50	610	670	467	568	465	221	60.0	-	-
30.5.35	40	25	440	395	155	1.00	1.50	545	605	492	558	495	215	57.5	-	-
30.5.35	40	35	460	400	135	5.50	5.75	590	625	464	563	500	229	59.5	2.74	975
30.5.35	40	35	455	395	130	5.50	5.75	620	650	463	570	505	234	61.5	2.45	900
30.5.35	40	35	460	400	130	5.50	6.00	635	665	467	575	510	240	61.5	2.49	916
30.5.35	40	45	440	365	90	6.00	6.25	605	620	-	544	500	261	60.5	2.33	846
30.5.35	40	45	450	355	95	6.00	6.50	615	640	-	544	495	268	61.2	2.81	1032
31.5.35	40	45	440	365	80	5.00	5.50	600	670	-	535	475	267	62.4	2.20	824
31.5.35	50	25	450	365	180	2.00	2.25	510	600	-	483	438	228	58.5	-	-

Date	HP cut off	LP cut off	Boiler	HP steam chest	LP receiver	Exhaust	Smokebox Vacuum	Smokebox temp	HP Super-heater temp	Receiver temp	LP Super-heater RH temp	LP Super-heater LH temp	Exhaust temp	Speed	Pull	Drawbar
D.M.Y	%	%	Psi No 1 bars	Psi	Psi	Psi	Inches	Deg F	Deg F	Deg F	Deg F	Deg F	Deg F	mph	tons	Hp
31.5.35	50	25	410	350	170	1.75	2.50	515	580	-	480	448	222	60.0	0.69	249
31.5.35	50	35	420	350	175	6.25	6.00	550	595	-	524	480	228	60.5	1.87	675
31.5.35	50	35	440	360	175	5.00	5.25	600	645	-	562	515	229	61.6	1.74	643
31.5.35	30	45	450	350	130	13.00	11.50	650	680	-	589	545	285	60.0	3.65	1314
31.5.35	30	45	475	380	140	15.50	12.75	700	700	-	594	550	299	61.5	4.00	1476
31.5.35	30	55	470	410	45	4.00	5.00	605	645	-	496	438	281	60.0	2.22	799
31.5.35	30	55	475	420	45	4.00	5.00	590	650	-	489	445	283	60.0	1.76	634
31.5.35	40	55	475	400	70	8.75	8.50	630	685	-	489	445	286	61.5	3.31	1247
31.5.35	40	55	480	400	70	8.00	8.00	660	680	-	500	455	287	60.5	2.78	1002
31.5.35	40	55	475	400	65	8.00	8.00	655	685	-	504	448	291	61.2	3.80	1395
31.5.35	40	55	445	370	60	7.00	7.00	655	670	-	497	455	289	61.5	2.47	948
31.5.35	50	55	420	350	95	7.75	7.75	560	645	-	465	425	243	49.5	4.67	1387
31.5.35	50	55	420	350	95	8.00	8.00	595	640	-	477	438	237	53.0	3.41	1084
31.5.35	50	55	410	345	90	7.50	7.50	620	665	-	491	448	242	52.0	4.03	1257

Blast pipe tests

Date	HP cut off	LP cut off	Boiler	HP steam chest	LP receiver	Exhaust	Smokebox Vacuum	Smokebox temp	HP Super-heater temp	Receiver temp	LP Super-heater RH temp	LP Super-heater LH temp	Exhaust temp	Speed	Pull	Drawbar
D.M.Y	%	%	Psi No 3 bars	Psi	Psi	Psi	Inches	Deg F	Deg F	Deg F	Deg F	Deg F	Deg F	mph	tons	Hp
4.6.35	30	55	450	405	85	0.50	1.25	485	605	355	457	410	210	56.5	0.78	262
4.6.35	40	35	460	380	110	2.00	4.00	535	605	380	445	418	220	60.0	2.68	960
4.6.35	40	35	460	395	110	2.00	4.00	550	620	390	454	428	219	60.0	2.60	930
4.6.35	40	35	440	375	105	1.75	3.75	585	650	410	469	435	218	61.5	2.31	847
4.6.35	40	45	425	350	80	2.25	4.25	620	675	420	510	495	224	60.0	3.21	1149
4.6.35	40	45	400	330	75	2.00	4.25	635	670	405	503	485	225	60.0	2.46	880
4.6.35	30	45	450	390	50	1.00	2.50	550	610	335	441	395	216	60.6	1.42	515
4.6.35	30	45	460	400	52	1.25	3.00	545	605	335	440	390	216	61.0	1.32	480
4.6.35	30	45	440	390	52	0.75	1.75	540	605	325	435	385	214	59.0	1.02	359
4.6.35	30	45	420	380	50	0.50	1.75	520	600	325	430	390	213	59.0	0.77	270
4.6.35	50	40	460	380	156	3.00	6.00	645	650	430	509	465	223	61.0	3.43	1250
4.6.35	50	40	440	350	148	3.00	5.50	665	650	445	519	475	222	61.0	2.88	1050
5.6.35	30	55	430	380	38	1.00	2.50	585	690	345	480	445	272	59.0	0.95	335
5.6.35	30	55	430	380	38	1.00	2.50	575	655	340	455	440	260	60.0	1.01	360
5.6.35	40	40	470	405	104	1.50	3.50	580	630	370	453	425	223	59.5	1.43	510
5.6.35	40	40	450	400	109	1.25	3.25	615	640	385	458	440	217	61.0	1.35	494
5.6.35	40	40	420	370	90	1.00	3.00	605	650	390	462	440	216	60.0	1.46	525
5.6.35	40	40	410	350	90	1.00	3.00	610	655	400	470	445	215	61.0	1.23	450
5.6.35	50	40	430	340	140	2.25	6.00	680	685	470	509	475	221	61.0	2.47	900
5.6.35	50	40	400	320	132	2.00	5.50	685	685	475	525	488	221	60.5	2.37	855
5.6.35	30	35	430	380	72	0.75	2.25	530	560	335	430	385	220	59.6	1.65	585
5.6.35	30	35	400	360	68	0.50	2.00	540	585	345	429	395	218	61.5	0.90	330

Date	HP cut off	LP cut off	Boiler	HP steam chest	LP receiver	Exhaust	Smokebox Vacuum	Smokebox temp	HP Super-heater temp	Receiver temp	LP Super-heater RH temp	LP Super-heater LH temp	Exhaust temp	Speed	Pull	Drawbar
D.M.Y	%	%	Psi No 3 bars	Psi	Psi	Psi	Inches	Deg F	Deg F	Deg F	Deg F	Deg F	Deg F	mph	tons	Hp
5.6.35	50	55	470	390	102	6.00	9.00	690	735	400	610	514	299	56.7	5.02	1702
5.6.35	50	55	455	375	94	4.50	7.50	700	670	385	546	505	260	50.4	4.79	1445
5.6.35	50	55	450	370	88	3.75	6.50	700	645	395	521	500	251	53.0	4.64	1476
6.6.35	40	45	425	370	82	1.50	3.50	540	610	370	422	425	231	59.5	1.54	545
6.6.35	40	55	455	400	68	2.50	4.50	540	590	345	470	435	243	61.0	1.79	655
6.6.35	40	55	440	380	60	1.75	4.00	605	630	350	445	430	232	62.1	2.01	745
6.6.35	40	55	430	370	60	1.75	3.75	610	640	345	440	430	229	60.0	2.39	864
6.6.35	40	40	440	370	109	2.00	4.00	600	710	385	526	445	311	62.0	1.78	660
6.6.35	40	40	400	350	92	1.75	3.50	630	670	395	498	465	245	59.0	2.26	797
6.6.35	40	40	410	355	96	1.75	3.75	625	660	395	475	460	227	60.5	1.74	630
6.6.35	40	40	410	350	92	0.75	3.75	630	640	395	480	455	222	62.5	2.57	960
6.6.35	50	40	450	335	140	6.00	9.00	705	680	455	532	465	236	61.0	4.11	1500
6.6.35	50	40	440	325	140	5.75	8.50	710	685	465	553	495	237	60.0	4.05	1450
6.6.35	50	40	430	320	140	5.50	8.00	710	680	485	560	514	243	60.5	3.70	1335
6.6.35	50	40	430	315	140	5.75	8.50	710	680	485	564	524	231	61.0	3.66	1334
6.6.35	50	45	475	365	128	6.50	9.75	655	735	475	595	534	305	63.0	4.15	1560
6.6.35	50	45	460	360	124	6.00	8.50	690	715	465	578	538	273	59.0	4.26	1500
6.6.35	50	45	450	350	120	6.00	8.50	705	700	465	566	534	265	59.5	3.89	1380
6.6.35	50	45	455	350	120	5.75	8.50	715	695	465	565	543	261	60.0	4.19	1500
6.6.35	50	45	455	350	122	6.00	8.75	720	695	465	563	534	259	61.0	4.36	1590
6.6.35	30	55	475	425	48	1.00	3.00	575	630	375	519	480	293	60.0	1.39	500
6.6.35	30	55	445	400	44	1.00	2.75	555	610	345	482	470	283	60.5	1.25	450